ACKNOWLEDGMENTS

Thank you to my millennial panelists. This book would not exist without your generous contributions.

Thank you to my generous crowdfunding campaign supporters:

George Charles Allen
Mike Douglas
Arno Wielders
Jerome Strach
Vincent Vazzo
Lyndsay Castle
Patrick O'Laughlin
Tom Carlon
Patrick Havel
Alex Lewis
Justin Kugler
Anna Lewarchik
Gary Bickford
Joseph Colaccino
John Powell
Tara Halt
John Mulnix
Luc Riesbeck
Barry Bonzack
Terrence Cooney
Jake Robins
Joe William Bowles II
Amber Hornsby
Mark Cooper
Mike Ash
Chelsea Partridge
Rabi Boundi
Paul Turner
Roberto E. Garcia
Eric Becnel
Mason Hall
Kelsi Singer
Logan Kennedy

Thank you to my editor, Bart Leahy.

RISE OF THE SPACE AGE MILLENNIALS

The Space Aspirations of a Rising Generation

Laura Seward Forczyk

ISBN: 978-1-7344622-0-3 (paperback)

ISBN: 978-1-7344622-1-0 (ebook)

Cover art by TryCreations.

Front cover photography by *Hubble Space Telescope* / NASA, ESA, and T. Brown (STScI).

Back cover photography by Florida Today.

Back cover photo background mural by Robert Wyland.

Book design by Aslam Khan.

Interior art by Caroline Juang.

Printed in the United States of America.

First printing edition 2020.

Published by Astralytical.

www.astralytical.com

DEDICATION

To my parents, Jack and Barbara, who made me a mi lennial and both supported and encouraged my pursu of space.

To my millennial husband, Nathan, who supports m and believes in me.

To my children, Josephine and Leonardo, born in a ne generation, who inspire me to think generationally for thos who will come after me.

Table of Contents

INTRODUCTION

Why A Book About Millennials?

We've all heard the stereotypes: Millennials are lazy. Millennials are self-centered. Millennials are impatient. Millennials aren't loyal to employers or careers. These formulas are so common they've spun-off satire stories bemoaning all the industries millennials are supposedly "killing" because of their lack of patronage or interest. From avocado toast to trigger warnings, millennials get a bad reputation from older generations.

How much do these stereotypes hold true in reality? Can an entire generation be painted with such a broad brush? Can generational differences be explained by newer technology, a changing world, the ages and stages of life millennials are in, and culture clashes? Are millennials in their twenties and thirties really very different from the previous generations at the same age? The millennial generation, born between 1981 and 2000, offers surprises for those who seek answers to these questions and more.

Enough with the negative stereotypes and comical generalizations. They have become so ubiquitous and clichéd, they ceased to have much meaning. To understand who millennials really are and what they represent, let's take a peek at some individual stories and perspectives. Or rather a hundred of them.

In this book, you won't find any stories about entitled, fragile young adults unable to make it in the real world. Here you will find hard-working individuals within the space sector who exhibit optimism, hope, adaptability, futuristic long-term thinking, and a desire to bring along everyone for the ride.

What is the millennial generation working toward in space? What scientific discoveries and new frontiers do millennials hope to uncover? What challenges, struggles, tools, and perspectives do millennials bring to the workplace? In short, what *are* they thinking? Keep reading as we blast off to explore space with our 100 millennial stars.

Introducing Our Millennial Panel

As a scientist, I crave data. I'm endlessly grateful to the more than 100 millennials – colleagues, friends, and new acquaintances – who graciously agreed to be interviewed for this book as part of our millennial panel. Panelists are approximately 60% male and 40% female. They represent many states within the United States of America and five additional countries. These individuals graciously gave their time, thoughts, and words to the questions pondered herein.

You will learn their stories. The undergraduate student working hard to pass their classes and participate in extra-curricular activities while contemplating the career possibilities ahead. The graduate student, a little burnt out but still pushing forward, building their expertise and looking ahead to the job market. The entry-level engineer thrilled to work in their dream career and gain real technical experience while navigating the complexities of workplace culture. The mid-career scientist hustling to write grant proposals and juggle research on multiple space missions, keeping an eye on the science priorities ahead. The young CEO taking a gamble building their own space start-up, struggling with capital but pushing forward to production and operations, doing good work in the space industry. The communicator trying to sum up complex technical topics for a wider, non-technical audience while ensuring the story is also engaging. Our millennial panelists represent many fields and career stages.

Much of the language used to tell their stories come

from their own words. With or without direct quotations, their own language is repeated in these pages when reflecting on their experiences, their opinions, their hopes, and their dreams. I've expanded on their stories by giving context to their individual accounts within the greater narrative of this book. But wherever possible, I have stayed true to their stories by using the same wording, expressions, and emphases they used when storytelling within their interviews. Their emotions and conclusions are poured out on these pages while I, the author, serve as an intermediary to tie the narratives together.

You will not find the stories of their whole lives in these narrations. You may note a lack of personal and professional details. These particulars have been omitted for greater anonymity. I've generalized panelists' locations to regions, states, or countries, except in the case of Washington, DC. In some cases, I've created fictional names for real individuals who requested greater protection.

These are snapshots: frozen moments in time to capture transient life stages and ever-evolving thoughts, opinions, and ideas. Most these interviews took place in 2016. Should follow-up interviews take place, many of these individuals will be in different places in life and perhaps hold different perspectives. Some students will have graduated. Some young professionals will have obtained new jobs or promotions within the space sector. Some have left the field altogether in a temporary change or a career pivot. And some have risen to greater successes within their careers, even founding their own companies or establishing their own laboratories.

I took care to diversify the interviews based on academic discipline, field of work, gender, and geography. However I was not always successful and biases remain. Given my own geographic location within the United States, the majority of panelists are also within the United States and represent a Western society perspective.

Intersections

In 2016, millennials became the largest generation in the U.S. labor force making up more than a third of the working population.[1] Much has been written on the struggles of millennials with our unfavorable job market, unemployment, unstable employment, underemployment, disloyal and exploitative employers, freelancing struggles, high student loan debt, high costs of living, and the high barrier of entry for career-track jobs. Most millennials will graduate or have graduated from higher education with a mountain of debt, borrowing money to gain the education required for the modern workforce when jobs are not guaranteed.

Experiences will differ from person to person based on their backgrounds and their nature. Most women in the workplace experience some level of sexual harassment, especially in male-dominated fields such as the space sector.

---

1 Fry, Richard. "Millennials are the largest generation in the U.S. labor force." Pew Research Center, 11 April, 2018. The millennial generation definition they use includes birth year range 1981 – 1997.

Most racial and ethnic minorities experience conscious and unconscious prejudices within and outside of the workplace. Worse, the discrimination compounds: a person with multiple lower power characteristics often report more instances of discrimination than a person with only one lower power characteristic. A millennial who is young and seemingly inexperienced is in itself a disadvantage when ageism, too, is in play.

It is impossible to touch on the lives of millennials without touching on these hidden truths, even if just in passing. However, here's a hint of good news: these truths are no longer so hidden. Millennials and generation Z are more likely to speak openly about these challenges and inequities and are more likely to value societal equality and tolerance.

The ghosts of generations past continue to haunt millennials: racism, sexism, sexual orientation and gender identity discrimination, religious discrimination, ageism, disability discrimination, xenophobia, socioeconomic inequality, and bigotry of all kinds.

Some of these topics may be touched on within these pages but they are for the most part outside the limited scope of this book. As you read, please keep in mind the intersectional challenges, privileges, imbalances, and personal struggles that may plague, limit, or benefit millennials' experiences and outlooks. These worthy topics could become whole books of their own but they will not be directly addressed within this book.

Dear Older-Generation Readers

A note for the older-generation readers: you might not agree with every statement and opinion in this book. You may even object to some of what you read. When reading the chapter on generational differences, you may find yourself getting wound up, dismissing the subject with, "Kids these days..." Note that I did not interview any "kids" as millennial sources. All sources were student or professional adults over the age of 18 whose experiences, opinions, and ideas are valid and worthy of being expressed. You may disagree with them but I urge you not to dismiss them. The intent of this book is to give them a voice.

Aren't the voices of other generations just as valid? Yes, of course! Books such as this one could be written about baby boomers, generation X, and to some extent, even generation Z. I encourage you to write such a book and will offer you support and advice if you choose to do so. Fair warning: this book took me three years to write.

Why Write This Book?

I never saw myself as a book author. I was born into the millennial generation, fell in love with the space sector, and trained as a scientist. My bachelor's and master's degrees are in astrophysics and my doctoral research is in planetary science. I have never formally studied the social sciences in higher education. Yet here I attempt to analyze a specific segment of human society. I explore intergenerational relationships, opinions, values, and perspectives. Please excuse any amateur mistakes and simplifications made because of my lack of formal training in sociology, anthropology, or similar fields.

My expertise is in space. I am the founder and owner of Astralytical, a space consulting firm. I am an analyst and subject matter expert in space science, space industry, and space policy. I serve a wide range of clients from individuals to companies, universities, local government, federal government, and foreign governments. I've researched at three NASA centers, facilitated ISS research payloads, flown research on two parabolic "Zero G" microgravity campaigns, conducted geological research in a meteor crater, and earned National Aerospace Training and Research (NASTAR) suborbital astronaut wings in ground training. I am a six-time U.S. Space Camp alumna, a NASA Academy alumna, and I'm proud to serve as a mentor in the Brooke Owens Fellowship program supporting undergraduate women and gender minorities in aerospace. Space is my passion.

As a millennial, I feel responsible to best represent myself and my peers as we truly are, not caricatures of our worst characteristics. I've turned to storytelling to enlighten the world as to who "space millennials" really are, what we believe in, how we best work, and what are goals and dreams are.

What You'll Find Inside

I asked our millennial panel several key questions to probe their opinions, preferences, and goals.

1. What inspires millennials in the space sector?
2. Why does humanity pursue space?
3. What destinations should astronauts aspire to visit next?
4. How should we approach human spaceflight?
5. Does mission length matter?
6. How risky is too risky?
7. How well do millennials multitask?
8. Do millennials collaborate internationally?
9. How do millennials use social media?
10. What generational differences do millennials see?
11. What do millennials aspire to accomplish in space?

Want to be inspired by the future space workforce? Read on. You'll learn the space sector is in good hands with the rising of space-age millennials.

ABBREVIATIONS

ARM	Asteroid Redirect Mission
CCP	Commercial Crew Program
CEO	Chief Executive Officer
COTS	Commercial Orbital Transportation Services
CRS	Commercial Resupply Services
DNA	Deoxyribonucleic acid
ESA	European Space Agency
FAA	Federal Aviation Administration
GPS	Global Positioning System
HST	Hubble Space Telescope
ISRU	In situ resource utilization
ISS	International Space Station
ITAR	International Traffic in Arms Regulations
KSC	Kennedy Space Center
JSC	Johnson Space Center
JWST	James Webb Space Telescope
LEO	low-Earth orbit
MSFC	Marshall Space Flight Center

NASA	National Aeronautics and Space Administration
SLS	Space Launch System
STEAM	Science, Technology, Engineering, Art, and Mathematics
STEM	Science, Technology, Engineering, and Mathematics
STS	Space Transportation System
TESS	Transiting Exoplanet Survey Satellite
WFIRST	Wide Field Infrared Survey Telescope

Generation Definitions

These are the generation definitions used for this book. These dates may differ depending on the source with only the Baby Boomer generation range being well agreed upon. For example, some consider generation Z beginning in the mid- to late-1990s whereas others consider generation Z beginning closer to 2004. The end range of generation Z and the beginning of a new generation, currently called generation alpha, has not yet been defined.

Greatest Generation	Born 1901 – 1927
Silent Generation	Born 1928 – 1945
Baby Boomers	Born 1946 – 1964
Generation X	Born 1965 – 1980
Millennials / Generation Y	Born 1981 – 2000
Generation Z	Born 2001 – present or undecided end date

CHAPTER 1
WHAT INSPIRES THIS GENERATION?

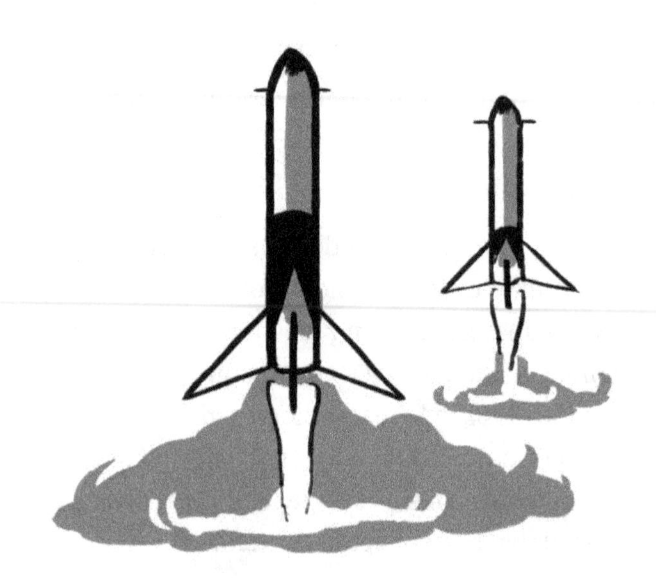

The Millennial Lifetime

Half a century ago, the Apollo Generation was born. The National Aeronautics and Space Administration (NASA) launched its Mercury (1958 – 1963), Gemini (1961 – 1966), and Apollo (1961 – 1975) programs. Science fiction and science reality proclaimed space the final frontier. New dreams were born and some became realized right in front of their eyes.

On July 21, 1969, Neil Armstrong and Edwin "Buzz" Aldrin placed the first human steps on the lunar surface while people back on Earth watched and the world got a little smaller. Suddenly, anything seemed possible. Newspapers the next day declared Mars the next destination for Earth voyagers. People living and working permanently in space seemed inevitable. The Apollo Generation was born.

In much the same way the greatest generation, the silent generation, the baby boomers, and their international equivalents were inspired by the Moon landings to work in and advocate for space exploration, younger generations, too, were inspired. But were younger generations inspired by Apollo, which for some generation Xers and all millennials had ended before they were born? For many, yes. The "giant leap for mankind[2]" left its footprint in our hearts and souls for generations to come. But many others found inspiration elsewhere.

Millennials have not experienced the unifying, transforming "Where were you when?" achievement of seeing a human step foot on another world for the first time, or for any time, except in archived footage. Millennials have not had the opportunity to begin a new space age from scratch, molding it in a fashion that represents the values and directions we believe would best carry humanity forward into the stars. Millennials continue to strive to push for inclusivity for those who were previously hidden or obstructed

2 Neil Armstrong's first words as he stepped foot onto the Moon were, "That's one small step for [a] man, one giant leap for mankind."

from participating in the dawn of the space age.

Millennials were born after the beeping of Sputnik, after Explorer 1 confirmed the Van Allen radiation belt, after Yuri Gagarin launched human spaceflight, after humans made one small step and one giant leap on the Moon, and after *Salyut 1* and *Skylab* housed humans in low Earth orbit (LEO).

The oldest millennials were born right as the Space Shuttle program started taking off. Most millennials are too young to remember the *Challenger* incident, but most painfully remember *Columbia*'s demise. The youngest millennials may be too young to even remember that.

The youngest millennials may have been born after the initial construction of the *International Space Station* (ISS), but all millennials were on Earth when the ISS welcomed its first long-term inhabitants in 2000. The ISS has been continuously inhabited for all of the youngest millennials' lives.

All millennials have witnessed the mounting evidence for water on the Moon and Mars, the rise of SpaceX and the NewSpace movement, the first detection of gravitational waves, and the birth of a new government space agencies in Algeria, Australia, Bahrain, Belarus, Bolivia, Colombia, Iran, Japan, Lithuania, Malaysia, Mexico, New Zealand, Paraguay, Philippines, Portugal, Saudi Arabia, South Africa, Thailand, Turkey, Turkmenistan, the United Arab Emirates, the United Kingdom, Uzbekistan, and Venezuela.

Millennials are on the rise, even in space itself. This

past year, 2019, saw the first millennial astronaut in space: Hazza Al Mansouri. At age 35, he became the UAE's first astronaut when he rode a Soyuz MS-15 to the ISS.. In the coming years, many more millennials will get their chance to experience space personally, both in government programs and in private space tourism flights.

A childhood spark can light a fire for a lifetime. For these lifelong dreamers, a single early event or concept can propel them space-bound. Some find joy and inspiration in space happenings throughout their lives, their collection of space balloons keeping them aloft and reaching up toward the stars. Others discover a love of space later in life, stumbling upon it or guiding their way back to it due to an influential event, activity, individual, or just stars aligning[3].

What inspired and continues to inspire millennials who pursue space? For some, the Apollo landings gifted the dream of exploring our nearest celestial neighbor, the beautiful orb in the sky that has captivated humanity throughout time. NASA calls those involved in the new push to return to the Moon the Artemis Generation. NASA's Artemis program envisions landing the first woman and the next man on the surface on the Moon – and soon. Governments, companies, and individuals around the world are inspired by similar efforts, notably the European Space Agency's Moon Village and the China National Space Administration's *Chang'e* program. All envision a future where Earthlings have finally transcended our home world and are liv-

3 Fear not, dear reader: this is a poetic figure of speech and not a nod toward astrology.

ing and working on the Moon. But don't stop there! Every humans-to-the-Moon initiative is understood to be as a precursor to a Mars program – and beyond.

NASA's Space Shuttle program (1981 – 2011) inspired many millennials, especially older millennials and those who worked directly with the program. For most millennials, the space shuttles were the iconic image of humans leaving the bounds of Earth in their lifetimes. In much the same way, the ISS program, the orbiting home to astronauts continuously since 2000, is most millennials' vision of space habitation, microgravity science, and international partnership. For millennials, the ISS is the only off-world destination humans have reached in their lifetime. Yet.

Then there's "NewSpace." It's more of a mindset than a category. There is no agreed-upon definition or start date for when this sort of space activity began. Generally speaking, NewSpace encompasses the emerging commercial space industry of the past couple decades, companies often founded by wealthy entrepreneurs whose goals are to soar to space mostly or entirely independent of government initiatives. Space Exploration Technologies Corporation (founded 2002), commonly known as SpaceX, is the clear leader of the NewSpace movement with its charismatic founder and CEO Elon Musk. Other notable human spaceflight companies include Jeff Bezos' Blue Origin (founded 2000), Richard Branson's Virgin Galactic (founded 2004), and Robert Bigelow's Bigelow Aerospace (founded 1998). These emerging space companies of the new millennium are the most frequently cited sources of inspiration for millennials.

For other millennials, and for humanity throughout history, life's big questions inspire them to seek and explore. Where did we come from? Are we alone? What is our place in the Universe? As technology improves and science progresses, those questions morph into specific mysteries to unravel. Are there any other planets like Earth? Are any other planets habitable for humans? What is dark matter? Dark energy? How did the Universe begin and how will it end? Or will it end? Even exploring the unknown craters, caves, and cryovolcanoes of planetary bodies within our Solar System is a frontier we're just beginning to probe.

More than learning what originally inspired millennials to pursue space, I wanted to know what keeps inspiring them. What activities are they performing or witnessing that make their studies, research, or work worth it every day? What about space excites them to get out of bed and keep working toward their dreams?

Childhood Inspirations

Mechanical engineer Tracie in Alabama was inspired to pursue space exploration in fifth grade when she saw the movie *Apollo 13*[4]. She grew up in a very rural area with NASA posters on her wall from trips to NASA's Kennedy Space Center (KSC) in Florida. She can hardly believe she now gets paid to do what she is so passionate about. It's a

---

4 *Apollo 13*. Directed by Ron Howard, Universal Pictures, 30 June, 1995.

rare thing to be able to live out your dreams, she sighs.

Tracie cheers on the growing private space industry, even from her NASA office. She doesn't like the characterization that relations between NASA and commercial launch service providers such as SpaceX are antagonistic. They are symbiotic, she insists, they have a mutually beneficial relationship. NASA needs cheap and rapid access to space and commercial launch service providers are well poised to meet that need, she explains. In her view, NASA should be at the edge of an ever-expanding sphere of space technology development. SpaceX, Blue Origin, and others are working with NASA to build a low Earth orbit (LEO) economy.

Tracie believes human spaceflight is one of the crowning achievements of our species. To her, it's miraculous to watch anything leave this planet. But little else motivates her more than the idea of humans living and working sustainably in space. Being able to sustain life in the harshness of space is a testament to the power of human ingenuity and engineering, she asserts. Humans have been space-dwellers since Soviet cosmonaut Yuri Gagarin launched to space in a Vostok 1 capsule on April 12, 1961. The anniversary of his historic flight is now celebrated worldwide as Cosmonauts Day, Yuri's Night, and the International Day of Human Spaceflight.

Tracie is particularly excited about her work on in-space manufacturing, that is, making things in microgravity such as materials and tools with the ultimate goal of making anything we need in space independently from Earth. If we are going to live in space, we need to make things there and on other planetary bodies rather than launching everything from Earth, she explains. Crew safety also depends on in-space manufacturing. Imagine being able to rapidly respond to those, "Houston, we've had a problem[5]," situations. Instead of jury-rigging a contraption to filter carbon dioxide from the air in the unforeseen *Apollo 13* crisis, future astronauts may be able to 3D print the devices they need in emergency situations. In-space manufacturing is also about shifting the paradigm from supply logistics toward sustainability, she clarifies.

Engineer Alex in Georgia won a scholarship in fifth grade to attend Space Camp at the U.S. Space & Rocket Center in Huntsville, Alabama. A dozen years later, he finds himself working in Huntsville, affectionately called the Rocket City, pursuing his NASA dream at Marshall Space Flight Center (MSFC). He is excited to watch private companies and NASA come together to achieve new heights in space exploration. He will be glued to the broadcast when the first crew on Boeing Starliner capsule and the SpaceX Crew Dragon capsule launch to space to dock with the ISS as part of NASA's Commercial Crew Program (CCP), both scheduled for 2020.

Engineer Paige in California recalls having a difficult

---

5 Commonly known as the quote, "Houston, we have a problem," by Tom Hanks' character of *Apollo 13* mission commander James "Jim" Lovell in the film *Apollo 13*, the true quote from the mission was, "Houston, we've had a problem."

time in high school accepting the end of the space shuttle program in 2011. The decision was made to fly the last space shuttle mission, STS-135, with no human-rated American vehicle successor yet operational. At the time, NASA hoped CCP partners Boeing and SpaceX would return American astronauts to the ISS after only a few short years' gap. Eight years later, we're still waiting. In the meantime, NASA has relied on its Russian partner Roscosmos to carry NASA astronauts to the ISS at a current cost of approximately $80 million per seat.

Paige wondered: Would the gap in NASA's ability to transport astronauts to space signal a decline in the space sector? She occasionally doubted her chosen career path was wise if space activity was on the decline. Thanks to the recent spike in space activity, her excitement has returned. She sees new astronaut-carrying launch vehicles rising to take the place of the space shuttle, vehicles such as NASA's Space Launch System (SLS) heavy lift rocket and Orion capsule as well as Dragon and Starliner. She is heartened by the collaboration between the public and private sector.

Aerospace engineer April in Texas dreamed of working for NASA all her life. Her role as "ISS pilot" is a dream come true, the next best thing to becoming an astronaut. The ISS is managed and operated by teams at NASA Johnson Space Center (JSC) Mission Control in Houston, Texas and elsewhere. She and her colleagues write blogs and social media feeds dedicated to space and volunteer their time at local events to promote space. To say she is passionate is an understatement, she laughs.

Innovative Inspirations

Aerospace engineer Logan in Alabama is working his dream job at NASA MSFC. He hopes to continue working there for his entire career. But it's the private industry that has him most excited, specifically a new "space race" of innovative technology and techniques. He holds up SpaceX as the poster child of increasing public interest in space through rocket reuseability. "Having frequent nail-biting first stage landing attempts keeps the attention of the casual space fan and the lofty colonization goal keeps true enthusiasts rooting for long-term success."

Although SpaceX was not the first to launch a rocket to space and land the spent booster gently, vertically back to Earth to be reused (Blue Origin takes that honor), it was the first to do so during an orbital mission. On December 21, 2015, SpaceX launched a Falcon 9 rocket delivering 11 satellites to orbit. Spectators watched in awe as the rocket's first stage navigated back to Cape Canaveral and landed upright on solid ground. SpaceX has since accomplished this feat many times, including the jaw-dropping Earthly safe return of two of Falcon Heavy's three rocket boosters simultaneously on February 6, 2018. The recovered boosters are refurbished and reused, sent to space again and again. The unofficial motto of reusable rocketry, coined by Blue Origin, is "launch, land, repeat."

Student and museum tour guide Walter in Florida is enjoying witnessing the transition to a new era from government-led space exploration to private ventures. Companies such as SpaceX, Blue Origin, and Virgin Galactic are establishing themselves by going out on their own, he notes, carrying the torch forward.

Engineer Mark in Virginia is energized by the private spaceflight boom. Governments have done most of the initial space development, he explains. He now sees governments stepping back while the private sector moves in to innovate.

Engineer Justin in Florida is heartened to see NASA "mature," that is, become more open to managing commercial ventures rather than doing everything themselves. In brief, there is a difference in the contracting mechanisms NASA is using to work with some of its newer commercial partners. Instead of NASA directing a contractor to build NASA-designed hardware, in some cases, NASA is purchasing services on commercial hardware. This gives commercial partners more freedom in development and the ability to sell those services to others. Justin credits Blue Origin and SpaceX with reducing the cost of spaceflight through reusable rocketry, an emerging technology that excites him.

Aerospace engineer Yasmin in Florida enjoys watching the new and exciting goals commercial space companies are pursuing. She admires the work SpaceX is doing to create less costly and more efficient space travel through reusable rocketry.

Astrophysics student Xzavier in Florida is inspired by SpaceX's recent successes with reusable rocketry. He watched as hard work, determination, and faith overcame obstacles that lead to their success safely returning spent rocket boosters back to Earth for reuse.

For engineer Nicholas in Texas, rockets are his life. He wants to bring the opportunity for space exploration to the common person. He believes reusable rocketry will make space travel more affordable. He credits the influx of investment in new reusable rocket technologies over the past 15 years for this progress. A recent college graduate, he believes he has more opportunities to develop new space technologies now than ever before.

Computer scientist Michael in New York is driven by space entrepreneurship. His favorite: SpaceX. He notes that Elon Musk has proven he can accomplish what he sets out to do. He dreams of buying a ticket to Mars with SpaceX someday. Elon Musk has long claimed he will retire on Mars. His primary motivation in founding SpaceX was to travel to the red planet. Michael wants to go with him to that exciting new world.

Michael is also inspired by public-private partnerships between NASA and the growing private space industry. He applauds NASA for increasing community and open-source involvement with initiatives like the Space Apps Challenge, an international hackathon (a rapid-paced software development event) using NASA data to solve problems on Earth and in space.

Space policy professional Nate in Washington, DC enjoys seeing complementary communities work together. Civil space agencies such as NASA and the Federal Aviation Administration (FAA), which regulates space vehicle launches and landings in addition to aircraft, are beginning to focus on activities beyond LEO. In 2016, private company Moon Express won approval from the FAA to place a robotic lander on the surface of the Moon at an yet-unscheduled date. While the FAA may not be the U.S. federal government entity to grant approval to private lunar landers in the future, it marked the start of a new era of private lunar exploration.

Nate notes that the private space industry is opening up opportunities for broader participation in LEO. He thinks both public and private space communities are finally moving toward their true potential, which has been decades in the making. This trend excites him. He envisions further discoveries and breakthroughs beyond LEO facilitated by governmental agencies and the expanded use of LEO by private industry where government has already paved the way.

Inspiring Dreams

Engineer Lindsay in Alabama is excited by the push towards reusable launch vehicles and spacecraft technologies. As commercial companies work to bring down launch costs, she believes we will see an increase in the accessibility of space for exploration, research, and tourism. "I would love to take a vacation in space one day, so this is great news for me!"

Lindsay is gratified to see private and government space programs working together to achieve human exploration beyond LEO. Sending cargo and astronauts to the ISS through CCP isn't the only way NASA and private space industry work together to send astronauts to space. She would like to see government and private space industry increasingly work together to establish a sustainable transportation infrastructure between Earth and the Moon including in-space fuel depots and resource outposts.

In situ resource utilization (ISRU), or living off the land, is one way NASA and some in the space industry hope to create a sustainable, profitable economy in space. In this case, "the land" includes the Moon, Mars, asteroids, and any other planetary body with resources humans or robots can obtain and use. This concept has created a so-far speculative space mining industry which includes two high-profile failed initiatives (Planetary Resources and Deep Space Industries) and several smaller, ongoing efforts.

Space mining and ISRU are heavily debated in legal communities working to balance the rights of a company to use and sell what they obtain, the ban against nations claiming sovereignty over celestial bodies as outlined in the 1967 Outer Space Treaty[6], and the concept of the global commons where all nations would directly benefit from space resources. Regardless of the legal implications, the most popular plan is to mine water on planetary bodies. Water ice can be used as water or be split into hydrogen

---

6 The Outer Space Treaty is more formally called the Treaty on Principles Governing the Activities of States in the Exploration and Use of Outer Space, including the Moon and Other Celestial Bodies.

and oxygen to be used as rocket propellant. The propellant can be stored in fuel depots in space to refuel passing rockets, saving on the fuel needed to land back on Earth and launch again.

Aerospace engineer Floyd in Iowa has his sights set on advanced propulsion methods, the kind that will get humans anywhere in the Solar System and enable us to soar to the stars. He envisions a space transportation system that uses fuel depots as waypoint stations for rockets carrying heavy payloads great distances. The gravitational pull of Earth requires rockets leaving our planet to expend a lot of fuel just to get into space. By stopping at a depot and stocking back up on needed propellant, rockets carrying heavy cargo or passengers could be able to travel farther in space than what has previously been possible.

Floyd's imagination is captured by even more futuristic propulsion systems such as Hyperloops and nuclear fusion. A Hyperloop is a high-speed tube transportation system proposed by Elon Musk and currently in the design and testing phase. Musk speculates this technology might be used on Mars as well as on Earth. Fusion rockets, propelled by energy emitted when atomic nuclei fuse together, are theorized to have a higher specific impulse than current chemical rocket propulsion systems.

More than an expensive human mission to a planetary body, Floyd supports technology development: the creation of space infrastructure such as the aforementioned fuel depots, asteroid mining, alternative launch systems, and any technology that can increase our space capabilities. Individually, these projects are less expensive than a grand human mission to Mars and can be beneficial to make such a mission more feasible and affordable.

Space communicator Calvin in New Mexico is driven by a desire to explore space to understand the unknown and learn as much as he can. He believes NASA is on the right path with human missions to the Moon before going on to Mars with the goal of sustaining human habitation on another world.

Mechanical engineer Chelsea in Florida is proud to support the effort to return humans to the Moon and someday set foot on Mars. She is gratified to see government agencies and private industry working together toward the same space goals. It's been slow going for so long, too long, she sighs. With a greater emphasis on public-private partnerships now, she believes we should be able to progress farther in space faster. Perhaps we can send humans on deep space missions in the not-too-distant future, she dreams. She calculates the return on investment will be greater if we thoroughly explore and research a new destination and create a sustained human presence wherever we dare to go.

Biomedical engineer Jordan in British Columbia feels addicted to solving technical space engineering problems as if they were puzzles. He believes the solutions will benefit all of humanity. He dreams of being an astronaut someday, perhaps even setting foot on Mars. He believes Mars is the best goal for human space exploration to inspire young lives, drive technological innovation, and focus everyone on a singular goal to advance humanity to a new frontier.

Engineer Tom in Florida takes pride in the kind of work he does. His job is his dream come true. He hopes his work and the work of others in the space industry inspire the nation. He sees NASA's outreach to students and the general public, such as their cool retro-inspired travel posters depicting scenes of humans exploring the landscapes of other worlds, spark that sense of national pride in others. Those scenes seem fanciful now, but someday, he dreams explorers really will visit those exotic lands. NASA is working to take us there, he proclaims.

As much as Tom dreams of a future of big rockets and human missions to Mars and other planets, he aspires for the tangible: the completion of the task in front of him. Having something to show for his work gives him the job satisfaction to keep on dreaming.

Millennials were born after thc excitement of Mercury, Gemini, and Apollo, Tom explains. The innovations of newer commercial companies such as SpaceX's reusable booster landings and its new Falcon Heavy rocket excite him more than routine rocket launches, even the ones he works on. He finds inspiration in new heavy-lift vehicles such as Falcon Heavy and SLS, carrying more and doing more.

Partnering to Inspire

Bioengineer Diana in California is excited by what she sees as synergies between NASA and the private space industry. Independent companies are able to develop NASA-initiated technologies for a fraction of the cost, a win-win for everyone, she cheers. In addition to the CCP partners contracted to carry astronauts to the ISS, NASA also developed the Commercial Orbital Transportation Services (COTS) program which led to the Commercial Resupply Services (CRS) program to contract SpaceX and Northrop Grumman (formerly Orbital ATK) to carry cargo to and from the ISS. By the end of 2019, SpaceX's Dragon capsule delivered 18 successful CRS missions with one failure and Orbital ATK/Northrop Grumman's Cygnus capsule delivered 10 successful CRS missions with one failure. Aside from high-profile missions to the ISS, NASA works with many private companies to contract out work and co-develop technologies needed for the Agency's missions.

Planetary scientist Ryan in Missouri is a passionate lunatic: that is, a planetary scientist researching the Moon and a lunar exploration advocate. She is enthusiastic about her job which allows her to do exactly what she wants to do. She hopes to grow in her career gaining more responsibilities and eventually becoming an astronaut.

Ryan is especially pleased to see the partnership between private companies such as SpaceX and NASA working together to deliver supplies through COTS and eventually humans through CCP to space. By themselves, she is skeptical that private companies can do what they claim to do until they have proven themselves. SpaceX's accomplishments with developing reusable launch vehicles to drive down costs excite her. She hopes other companies such as Blue Origin have similar successes. She finds it encouraging to know that commercial spaceflight will continue regardless of what happens with government funding.

Democratization of Space

Aerospace engineer and businessman Ethan in Alabama is inspired by commercial space companies contributing to democratizing consumer markets. He foresees a future where spaceflight business enterprises enable the development of a spacefaring society. He believes Earth orbit is the primary domain for developing business opportunities with the next potential domains being cislunar space and the lunar surface.

Corporate communicator Evan in Washington, DC realized his calling to work in space two years after graduating when he found himself reading and blogging about the space industry every day. He participated in every space activity he could and networked hard until landing his first gig in the space industry. His work excites, educates, and fascinates him, something he can't put a price on. He truly loves getting up for work every day.

Evan is excited to witness the democratization of space via the rise of commercial space companies. Even though they are still very much supported by the government, he is encouraged to see private companies driving some of the space agenda. He believes humanity will benefit from billionaires investing in space initiatives. He is particularly inspired by Elon Musk, Jeff Bezos, Richard Branson, and Robert Bigelow. He foresees private companies continuing to help set the agenda for national space programs. He sees these innovative emerging space companies, "captivating our generation in a way unseen since the Apollo Era."

Human factors engineer Victor in Texas has always been fascinated with how humans live and perform in space. He believes humans should have a much larger presence in space by now. He is attracted to the commercial space industry because of its "not taking no for an answer" kind of attitude regarding space exploration.

Victor is pleased to see the commercial space industry increase the frequency of launches. Whether the destination is suborbital space, orbital space, the Moon, or Mars, he is happy to enter a new era in spaceflight filled with individuals who are making successful efforts toward a larger human presence in space.

Amy in Virginia is a scientist turned aerospace engineer. Her position gives her the advantage of working for multiple missions and projects spanning multiple programs that feed off each other. She strongly believes humanity should be working more in space than we already are. She is eyeing the commercial space industry to progress us outward.

Business consultant Liam in Virginia is an advocate for the social sciences in space, especially when imagining future human space settlements. He is excited by the increasing inclusion of cross-disciplinary professionals in space discussions and projects. People of all backgrounds and experiences bring value to the space sector, he insists. Human space missions benefit from those who study humans, he explains, and varied experiences can bring different perspectives to the conversation.

Engineer and world traveler JP is encouraged by the competition between private space companies. For any business to survive long-term, they must identify and execute a profitable business plan, he explains. Numerous niche markets have sprouted in the past decade. Suborbital space tourism, designer spacesuits, CubeSats, small satellite launchers, reusable launch vehicles, and asteroid mining companies are examples of newer technologies where businesses are now competing. Competition necessitates perfecting existing capabilities, trying new concepts, and accepting greater risk of failure to accomplish the ultimate goal of staying in business, he explains. He knows some companies will fail, but some will find a way to turn a profit and perhaps become the next multibillion-dollar giant of the space industry.

Improving Life

JP is excited by the science and state-of-the-art technologies coming out of government space programs. Space-based telescopes, rovers, landers, and probes take us to uncharted territories containing untold secrets, he gushes. There are no business plans for these types of missions and he understands it's hard to quantify their value. However, for visionaries who see humanity's future among the stars, he believes these programs are priceless.

JP is motivated by the vision of stepping onto another

planet such as Mars. He envisions a settlement on another world supporting tens of thousands of people working together toward a common goal. He advises this coalition of scientists, engineers, policymakers, and others to rise above their differences and cooperate in ways that will inspire generations to come.

Engineer Alex in Alabama has grand visions and a warning for the growing space industry: don't create any space bubbles that will pop while this growing industry is still getting off the ground. "There is too much capital put into space technology to have it implode because of investor greed." He believes we need to cooperate more than we compete. In doing so, he hopes we will become a multi-planetary spacefaring species.

Engineer and CEO Jay in Alabama is inspired by the social good that stems from government and private space programs. "The prospects of helping people in need through space is exciting to me." It's important to him that his job creates real value for the space industry as well as others outside of it.

Aerospace engineer Darius in Alabama enjoys working on cutting-edge technology to take humankind further than ever before. He gets satisfaction from knowing that the problems he is working to solve can help people around the world. His passion for space got him through long hours and all-nighters in college. Now he's working the kind of space geekery he always wanted to do. He can't see himself working in any other career.

Satellite engineer Adam in Colorado is inspired by his career which influences people all around the world. His job involves helping keep Earth orbit safe for current and future spacecraft, an increasingly important job as space activity increases.

Aerospace engineer Christopher in Colorado is inspired by the innovative emerging space industry, especially SpaceX, Blue Origin, and Virgin Galactic. These NewSpace companies and others are changing the way we perceive space exploration, he explains. He also supports Earth observation satellites which give us a greater understanding of our changing planet and help us to preserve Earth for future generations. He sees great value in Earth observation satellites for environmental conservation efforts, sustainable practices, and informing public opinion on environmental issues.

Engineer Lyndsay in Virginia appreciates the technology developed due to space exploration. New technology benefits life on Earth now as well as plans for future space settlements. Daily she's excited to read news headlines regarding game-changing space technologies. She's thrilled to see so many varied new ventures in the space industry.

Impressive Growth

Engineer and data scientist Nikolai in the Czech Republic is fascinated by the growth of the space industry. He tracks it all. He has been collecting data for years, terabytes of information on companies pursuing space development. An engineer by training, Nikolai now spends much of his time analyzing the impressive space market expansion and wondering if there is a space economic bubble forming. He can barely keep up with all the new players and industry changes. Perhaps one day very soon, it will be beyond his abilities to track it all by himself.

With so much space activity forming and growing, Nikolai can't help himself – he has to get involved. He has his hands in multiple companies and he volunteers in several space advocacy organizations. He even founded his own space company.

Engineer and CEO Mark in Kentucky is excited by the rate of change in the space sector. He points to new companies popping up doing smallsat constellations, data analytics, asteroid mining, space transportation, and launch vehicles of all classes. Fewer people are needed to start a space company due to better collaborative working software and computer analysis tools, he explains. Those tools coupled with a more risk-tolerant investment environment have created an exciting time for Mark to be in the space industry. He foresees a coming shake-out in which some companies will make the wrong bet, won't be able to execute their plans, or are outmaneuvered by their competitors. However, he bets there will also be winners. He started his own company based on that bet.

Software engineer Brandon in Washington is amazed by how many space programs and companies currently exist. He sees the space industry now where the young airline industry was before it achieved inexpensive and reliable air transportation. With so many companies and initiatives trying different architectures and technologies in space, "no doubt, many will fail. Hopefully at least a few will pan out."

Aerospace engineer Eric in Alabama is intrigued by the multiple approaches to common space goals, each with their own strengths and weaknesses. With difficult and ambitious objectives, companies take substantial risks. He sees some paying off.

Engineer and businessman Dan in Pennsylvania is, "thrilled by the renaissance we're seeing on so many fronts in the space sector." He notes a bipartisan consensus for the United States to send astronauts beyond Earth orbit. He sees big and small space companies innovating with new business models and significant private investment flowing into entrepreneurial ventures. As a young professional, Dan is excited to see so much energy and innovation after what he saw to be decades-long programmatic inertia. He believes we will look back on this time as a significant transition for the space sector. He advises millennials to take responsibility to ensure it's a successful transition.

Safety engineer Rachel in Florida is captivated by various interpretations of space adventures. As an artist and an engineer, she is able to use her creativity in pursuing the sciences.

Rachel is inspired by private industry charging forward with space exploration and achievement. More professionals, companies, investors, and students are interested in contributing to space missions now than ever before, she says. "It is a refreshing cycle of inspiration, contribution, and achievements."

Emerging Opportunities

Businesswoman Carolyn in Colorado lights up when considering the broader picture of humanity's developing relationship with space internationally. She is especially excited by the rapid pace of emerging, diverse space projects. New opportunities to pursue grand and small space ideas allows for a new level of innovation, she adds. And who knows where that will lead.

Altynay in New York is an engineer with an interest in international space law. As a non-US citizen, she is heartened by the increase in opportunities in commercial space companies where she and others may someday find employment, not limited to government space agencies. She also foresees a more open and transparent space sector.

Biology student Skye in Florida sees opportunities blossoming in front of her. She sees the future of space exploration as endless with more and more companies coming into play. Every day people such as herself may be able to experience space for themselves.

To date, seven people have flown eight space tourism missions to the ISS from 2001 to 2009 with one private astronaut flying twice. Since then, space tourism has been more of a dream than a reality. But times are changing. Virgin Galactic flew five of its employees on two SpaceShipTwo suborbital flights in 2018 and 2019 in preparation for commercial operations. Over 600 people have purchased tickets for their suborbital space tourism flights. Blue Origin also plans to fly passengers in its suborbital New Shepard rocket. SpaceX has booked a space tourism flight around the Moon on its Starship heavy-lift vehicle with additional plans to fly space tourism flights suborbitally, orbitally, and to the Moon and Mars. In 2019, NASA created new guidelines for SpaceX and Boeing to fly paying customers on their Crew Dragon and Starliner capsules, respectively, which may include space tourism flights. Private space stations are in the works by companies Bigelow Aerospace, Axiom Space, and others. The dream of the average person floating in and perhaps vacationing in space is alive and well.

Engineer Nathan in Colorado is a big fan of space tourism. He hopes space tourism will offer society two needed perspectives: humility and objectivity. He is of the opinion space humbles people who look down on all of human existence and begin to realize how insignificant we are on a universal scale. Additionally, space prompts the question of how we got there, he says, guiding us to notice a world outside of outside of ourselves.

A self-professed space enthusiast, engineer and space policy professional Jane in Texas longs to accomplish her dream of traveling to space. Unfortunately, she laments, she was not born into the Hilton family. She does not have the riches to afford tens of millions of dollars to travel to the ISS, or a quarter of a million dollars to fly suborbitally via Virgin Galactic, or even tens to hundreds of thousands of dollars to fly to near-space on a high-altitude balloon.

However, look at that cost decrease, Jane notes. "The fact that the cost has so drastically increased is a testament to how much closer my dream might be!" She is confident that if private space travel continues in this direction of declining prices, average citizens such as herself will have the opportunity to travel to space. "I would hands down drop my life savings for the chance!"

Aviator Christopher in Florida dreams of the day when he can fly a suborbital spacecraft just as he does in the suborbital spaceflight simulator he runs. In fact, he's looking forward to taking multiple suborbital flights in a single day as well as visiting the Moon, Mars, and other destinations such as Europa. He expects we will need to establish space stations with artificial gravity and radiation protection at the Lagrange points (gravitationally stable locations in space) to travel greater distances. The human body is particularly vulnerable outside of Earth's atmospheric and magnetic field protection and in microgravity conditions away from our familiar 1 g environment.

Aerospace engineer Mason in Alabama sees more opportunities now than ever before to participate in space. Whether it's working for NASA, a government contractor, or one of the many startup companies bringing change to the field, he sees something for everyone in today's space industry. He believes there's a place for anyone who wants to get involved. Low-cost small satellites on smallsat launchers and increasing commercialization of the ISS gives students and researchers unprecedented opportunities to put their hardware in space for science experimentation and technology development, he explains. Access to space is becoming more available to everyone.

Mason is most excited to see human spaceflight becoming routine. He wants to see new and exciting activities in the Earth-Moon system such as private tourism, research, manufacturing, and resource gathering.

Computer engineer Joslyn in Florida is watching space transportation mature with great interest. More affordable and accessible launches and LEO missions will pave the way for regular and safe consumer spaceflight, she explains. "Cheaper missions would increase the volume of launches that may drive down the cost of scientific payloads that could be utilized by more universities and smaller private companies."

Physicist Lindsey in Maryland feels lucky as a millennial to work at a time when the private space sector holds such promise. She notes the increase in access to space due to CubeSats. These affordable and relatively simple small satellites measuring 10 cm by 10 cm by 11.35 cm, a little larger than a softball, are a great educational "starter pack" for students. Cubesats can be designed and built at varying levels of customization and sophistication. Even simple CubeSat projects may yield meaningful scientific results.

The ISS is also becoming more accessible, Lindsey adds. Academic and private researchers are able to explore microgravity science in ways beneficial to technology development, fundamental research, medicine, and life on

Earth. She cites Nanoracks as an example of a small business that helps to facilitate increased research in microgravity.

Cosmic Inspirations

Engineer Kyle in Washington is cheering on the private space sector. "I think the private sector is really driving the momentum in human spaceflight." He applauds the numerous companies working on human launch systems, revolutionizing capabilities that drop costs and increase launch cadence. Scientific exploration benefits from greater spaceflight accessibility, he explains.

Kyle is also excited by NASA's robotic Solar System exploration including successful robotic explorers *Cassini* (launched in 1997 to Saturn), *New Horizons* (launched in 2006 to Pluto and other Kuiper belt objects), and *Curiosity* (launched in 2011 to Mars). He is proud to have played a very minor role in the *James Webb Space Telescope* (JWST), a visible and infrared observatory scheduled to launch in 2021. He is looking forward to JWST teaching us more about the Universe. Pushing the boundaries of our knowledge is what space exploration is all about, he explains. He knows we will find answers, but most of the time we will be left with more questions which will guide us in our quest for further understanding.

Astronomer Jen in Arkansas is looking forward to space travel becoming more common and less costly. She is particularly interested in sending probes outside of our Solar System. She also supports a human mission to Mars to explore the effects of prolonged space travel on the human body. She is looking forward to a robotic mission to Jupiter's fourth largest moon Europa to search for life in the subsurface saltwater ocean below the icy crust. The Europa Clipper mission will launch a probe to orbit Jupiter and fly-by Europa perhaps as soon as 2025 followed by a potential Europa Lander mission in the future.

Geology graduate student Gabe in Arizona has a self-described selfish desire to understand the Universe. He admits that his passion may not cure human ailments or provide drinking water to developing countries. But he believes the endeavors of a curious planetary scientist are valuable to humanity and worthy of public funding.

Gabe praises the way private space companies have opened up competition in the marketplace to drive down space exploration costs and encourage innovation. These private initiatives provide next-generation scientists and engineers with lucrative positions, he adds. Relatively lucrative, anyway.

Engineer Vito in Colorado praises what he sees as a silver age of exploration due to planetary science missions. We have sent spacecraft to many distant planetary bodies including Vesta, Ceres, and Pluto. We will soon explore Europa and return samples from Mars. The Mars 2020 rover scheduled to launch in 2020 will collect martian geological samples to be retrieved and returned to Earth by a future mission.

Vito is also inspired by the growth of private space endeavors. He has been watching Blue Origin and SpaceX progress rocket reuseability technology with interest.

Astronomer and astrobiologist Giada in Maryland pursues the question, "Are we alone in the Universe?" Unless life is very rare, she believes we have the capability to build the technology to answer this question within her lifetime. She has been fascinated by planets since she was a kid and now researches planets in other star systems called extrasolar planets or exoplanets. She is looking forward to the next generation of large space telescopes to be able to directly image exoplanets and search for biosignatures in their atmospheres. Biosignatures are the elements, isotopes, and molecules we seek to observe that may provide evidence of past or current life.

Astrobiologist Joshua in California is crazy about exoplanets. He is dedicating many years of his life to the search for life on strange new worlds orbiting other stars. With the help of large space telescopes, he hopes we will soon make a discovery that would revolutionize our understanding of the cosmos. If we managed to find biosignatures and confirm life on even just one nearby exoplanet, statistically speaking, this may mean that our Universe is teeming with life. Thanks to these new space telescopes, it's more likely that a big discovery will be made within the span of his career than ever before. It's an exciting time to be alive, he exclaims.

Joshua is equally excited about the progress we've made getting life off Earth. Everything about SpaceX excites him from its successful landings of reusable rocket boosters to its plans for human Mars missions to its Falcon Heavy and Starship heavy-lift rockets. He is also looking forward to NASA's SLS heavy-lift rocket for the same reasons: opening up the potential of human spaceflight.

Astronomer Brett in Queensland is fascinated by dwarf planet Pluto. NASA's *New Horizons* space probe, which flew by Pluto for the first time in 2015, unveiled just how fascinating and dramatic of a world Pluto really is, he explains. Who knew that Pluto would have such interesting morphological surface features? A little closer to home, he is a fan of the rover *Curiosity* exploring the surface of Mars. Much farther from home, he is excited by the thousands of transiting exoplanets discovered by the Kepler Space Telescope and other observatories.

Astrobiologist Marie in California has a passion: expanding human presence in space via robotics. Robotic exploration has benefits over human exploration, she explains. Robots can orbit and fly by multiple planetary bodies. Robots can do science on the surface of these worlds for years and years. Robots can work in extreme environments where humans could never go.

Marie describes how new robotic missions can unveil some of the mysteries of our Solar System: How was it formed? How has the climate of Venus changed over time? Is there water on Mars? Which outer planet moons have liquid water oceans? What unknowns are still to be discovered in the Kuiper belt and beyond? The science possibilities fascinate her. She hopes we could discover all this and more with robotic space missions.

Being a scientist is a lifestyle for Marie. She's passionate about the job that pays her bills, and she's equally passionate about her side projects and the non-paid work expected of scientists including travel, peer reviewing scientific papers for journals, organizing events, consulting and focus groups, and being active in the scientific community. So deep is her passion, she previously gave her time to career work for free, working totally unrelated jobs to pay the bills while she built her desired career. Her dedication has paid off. She can't imagine a career anywhere else but the space sciences.

Planetary scientist Kelsi in Colorado is passionate about the robots we send into the far reaches of the Solar System. In her opinion, we should focus our resources on a more complete survey of our Solar System through robotic science missions rather than spending resources on human space exploration. There are many destinations in the Solar System we have never seen or have only had limited views. Every time we send a robotic science mission to somewhere new, we are surprised by what we find. She points to plumes on Enceladus and giant plains of convecting nitrogen ice on Pluto – no one expected those. "This challenges us to be open minded about what can, and does, occur in our solar system, and also provides comparisons to better understand physical processes that also occur on Earth."

Astronomer Crystal in Maryland is looking forward to the next era of space telescopes. Both JWST and the *Wide Field Infrared Survey Telescope* (WFIRST) are set to produce some amazing results once they are launched, she enthuses. She foresees the *Hubble Space Telescope* (HST), launched in 1990, continuing to produce amazing science as well.

To software manager Sarah in New Hampshire, the Universe is vast. We are insignificant in comparison in the grand scheme of things. The beautiful and mysterious images sent back from space telescopes remind her of our place in the cosmos, putting our smallness into perspective. She's looking forward to the upcoming launch of JWST for just this reason. Beyond the nearby destinations of the Moon and Mars, we have so much left to explore, she dreams.

Geology graduate student Sean in Arizona is heartened to see space missions receiving ample publicity thanks to social media. He is also pleased to see the high-priority goals of the 2011 Planetary Science Decadal Survey moving forward. The National Academies of Sciences, Engineering, and Medicine publish a report every decade identifying the key questions and priorities of the planetary science community. They also publish a separate Decadal Survey on Astronomy and Astrophysics and a Decadal Survey for Earth Science and Applications from Space.

Aerospace engineer Thais in Florida took an astronomy class in high school that opened her eyes to the Universe. Since then, she has been committed to exploring it. She frequently spends evenings looking up at the stars with one of her many telescopes, wanting to explore the unknown. She believes as a society, we explore space because we are curious. We all want to explore the unknown.

Astrophysicist Jacob in the United Kingdom is drawn to exploring the unknown. Space is the ultimate unknown. What we find out there may completely change how we perceive ourselves here. That's what motivated him to study physics in graduate school.

Personal Inspirations

Geodesist Ryan in Colorado is more motivated by the immediate problems he is trying to solve than by the bigger picture of his work. As a scientist, he is pleased his research impacts meteorology, hydrology, and climatology. "This is gratifying, but the greatest pleasure of my work comes from wrangling and visualizing data and developing novel applications for it. The satisfaction of the impact of my work is simply secondary to the day-to-day satisfaction of seeing a model I created accurately predict data or creating a succinct visualization of a complex dataset or problem."

Launch and landing engineer Adam in Florida feels privileged to have worked on a major milestone – launch – of many missions. He admires those who were already working those missions for years, dedicating so much of their life to their project before it even left the ground. He is inspired by the new discoveries these missions bring, as well as the science and technology that stretches how far we can go and what we can learn.

Space exploration is a passion and "first love" of aerospace engineer Kelly in Florida. She wholeheartedly believes in space exploration. She would do her job for free so long as she could say she worked on something that helped carry humankind into space.

Public Inspirations

Astronomer Rodrigo in New York is so passionate about his job, he would probably keep doing it even if he wasn't getting paid. He wholeheartedly believes in expanding the frontiers of human knowledge through science and bringing the public along on the journey of discovery. Modern space programs are continuously pushing boundaries and achieving things that were once only possible in science fiction, he exclaims. And these achievements are doing a fantastic job at increasing public enthusiasm. He points out that increasing public knowledge about astronomy and space exploration attracts both public and private funding to the field which enables all the amazing science that's happening right now.

Aerospace engineer Anthony in California prioritizes public excitement for space. He sees fickle public opinion dwindling quickly after major space missions. The more space activities occur, the more public pays attention, he explains. He's thrilled by companies such as SpaceX and Virgin Galactic who are buzzing up the public. Soaring space popularity may mean soaring space funding.

Science reporter Leah in Massachusetts delights in the cycle of the public's space excitement. Her work is to inform the public about groundbreaking space achievements. When a member of the public gets excited about a mission, they are more likely to care about the important progress being made and science being done in space. This in turn focuses government funding and investor attention on public and private space activities. Increased collaboration between the government and private space sector brings reality closer to her vision of the private space industry becoming more mainstream. "The more 'mainstream' the space industry becomes, the more it can accelerate!"

Biologist David in California can't believe he's paid to work his dream job. He is proud that a portion of the U.S. government is dedicated to scientific exploration and understanding our place in the Universe. "NASA remains such a powerful symbol and give me hope for the future of humanity." He contributes a tiny step along the way, knowing he will pass the torch to the next generation when he retires. Exploration is never complete.

Barry in Florida is a businessman who throws himself into his passions. He's working his dream job witnessing history in the making with a front row seat to help plan it, tell its story, and make it happen. There's nowhere else he'd rather be.

A new acronym has emerged over the past decade: STEAM. Related to STEM (science, technology, engineering, and mathematics), STEAM adds an A for art to encourage a different kind of creativity. Design engineer Rachel in Florida is an artist as well as an engineer. This duality of "right brain" and "left brain" skills has proven useful in her career. She can design a space-related robot and tell its story to help others understand her work. She enjoys learning through photography, illustrations, and writing. The diversity of communication styles allows her to continue improving her skills beyond her formal engineering education.

We are all inspired by something or someone, perhaps a grand mission, perhaps a personal goal, perhaps a role model. Rachel finds inspiration from a brazen, fearless engineer and entrepreneur: SpaceX's Elon Musk. "I have a celebrity crush on Elon Musk. I love his brazen, fearless approach. I see him doing more than just energizing space exploration itself; I see him inspiring my generation to be bold and fearless in the face of 'impossible' missions." She is inspired by his mission to produce meaningful work, both within SpaceX and his automobile company Tesla. "Because what's the point of doing any of this if it's not making life better somehow?" she asks.

The storyteller in Rachel also find inspiration in NASA's upcoming next-generation Great Observatory: JWST. Similar to Hubble, JWST will image the Universe, giving humanity what she calls "mind-blowing" images of space that ordinary people can appreciate. She believes it's human nature to freely explore and expand our understanding of the external world and to expand our understanding of ourselves. Space observatories can become storytellers, she explains. Astronomical imaging makes visible the celestial phenomena we could never see with our own eyes, she adds. Not everyone understands the technical points of science and engineering, but she knows if she shows someone a space photograph, they will get it. She can't wait to see what JWST brings back.

While exploring the wonders of the Universe, we can't

lose sight of the wonders around us, Rachel warns. She is blown away by all the beauty and diversity we are privileged to enjoy on Earth. She marvels at the possibilities on other planets. She believes Mars is the next practical step for human space exploration and expects to see humans land boots on the surface of the red planet in her lifetime. But she also hopes to go beyond. She is pining for a major breakthrough in rocket propulsion in her lifetime so we can visit Earth-like planets currently too far from our reach. She points to that smaller space observatory Kepler which saw worlds we humans cannot with our own eyes: thousands of exoplanet candidates. New propulsion methods may be able to propel humans beyond our Solar System into star systems beyond, she dreams, to the very planets we are now discovering. She wants to see what life looks like when nature is given similar-but-different environmental conditions. Nature is so creative, she muses.

Is nature creative enough to give rise to intelligent life beyond Earth? Rachel ponders what intelligent life evolving on another world would look like. Would they seem human-like or be totally different? She can't wait for the encounter of a "third kind"[7] and the mental shift that comes with that new reality. A spookier reality to her would be a Universe with no intelligent life other than ourselves. To her, that seems off. Are we in a computer simulation, she wonders? Her questions are as endless as space itself.

---

7 In the 1977 Columbia Pictures *film Close Encounters of the Third Kind* written and directed by Steven Spielberg, an encounter of the "third kind" meant an alien observation.

My Inspirations

I was inspired in childhood by science fiction and the Apollo program. The concept of humans exploring the Moon intrigued me. That could be me, I dreamed. Attending Space Camp in Huntsville, Alabama four times as a kid (and twice more as an adult) fueled my passion of exploring the stars. I wanted to understand how the beauty of creation came to be and I wanted to travel there myself.

It wasn't until graduate school studying astrophysics and planetary science was I introduced to the roller coaster worlds of space entrepreneurship and space policy. Private companies were creating their own space vehicles and flying private individuals on space tourism adventures. I could do that! Almost accidentally, I entered the world of space entrepreneurship, combining my love of space sciences and the new reality of the emerging private space industry. The Moon will always be my first love and my first choice, but suborbital space seems most obtainable for someone like me. Somehow, someday, some way, I'll make it to the stars. *Ad astra*[8].

Inspirations of a Generation

Millennial space inspirations are broad and varied. A few millennials were inspired by the stories of Apollo and the history of the Space Age. Some millennials were inspired by NASA as children, aspiring to pursue their dream

---

8 *Ad astra* is a Latin phrase meaning, "to the stars." It is also the motto of the National Space Society.

jobs in the space sector. And achieved their dreams they did.

Many millennials are inspired by NASA's recent and current astronomy and planetary science missions. From the mysterious astrophysical phenomena captured by *Hubble* and other observatories, to the far-traveling *New Horizons* and *Voyager* probes, to the glimpses of distant exoplanets, and everything in between, our views of the Universe capture our imaginations.

By far, the top inspiration for millennials has been the emergence of the commercial space industry and its superstar: SpaceX. With feats never before seen such as landing two rocket boosters back to the ground simultaneously, to public-engaging showmanship such as launching a Falcon Heavy carrying a Tesla Roadster with a spacesuited mannequin playing David Bowie music, it's no surprise SpaceX motivates and excites millennials entering and growing in their space careers.

Other private space ventures, from Blue Origin's large ambitious to CubeSats' small and accessible technology, make a big impact on the space sector and the minds of millennials. For many millennials, their ultimate goal is to better humanity. Some conclude that to make the world a better place, we need to go off-world.

CHAPTER 2
WHY WE BOLDLY GO

Why Space?

Why do we explore space? What is it about distant celestial objects that seem to call out to us on our lively blue planet? Why do we spend the money, exert the effort, and in some cases risk lives in our pursuit of the mysteries beyond Earth? Why do we care?

Space benefits us. Space offers practical solutions to our Earthly lives, from ancient navigation by the stars to helpful timekeeping based on predictable orbits to modern-day navigation, broadcasting, and Earth observation satellites. The list of historic, current, and near-term future benefits of space to human life on Earth is so long, it would fill the contents of another book.

Beyond the discernible solutions space offers humanity are the intangible desires to reach out into the unknown. Although I know of no way to quantify it, insatiable curiosity and the seductive spirit of exploration are commonly cited as reasons why pioneers push outward, risking lives and livelihood. We seek. We question. We discover. The moment we choose to stay home on *terra firma*[9] is the moment we stop growing.

The early space age of the 20th century was dominated by the geopolitics of World War II and the Cold War. Governments invested in developing space technology and operations to gain advantages over their adversaries. Citizens cheered their respective nation's space achievements in a collective patriotic pride, although not universally. Public support for NASA's Apollo program never rose above 50% at the time. Yet when *Apollo 11* landed Armstrong and Aldrin on the Moon, people around the world felt a sense of pride in what humans can achieve.

What conversation about the motivations to explore space would be complete without quoting President John F. Kennedy, "We choose to go to the Moon. We choose to go

---

9 *Terra firma* is Latin for "solid earth" and is used here in a double-meaning to refer to our planet as well as solid ground.

to the Moon in this decade and do the other things, not because they are easy, but because they are hard, because that goal will serve to organize and measure the best of our energies and skills, because that challenge is one that we are willing to accept, one we are unwilling to postpone, and one which we intend to win, and the others, too."[10] Undoubtedly, for many, we pursue space because it's the next greatest challenge before us.

I asked our millennial panel why we humans choose to pursue space. The reasons they gave are as diverse as the panel itself although many ideas overlap. We may be driven by different motivations but we all work toward the same goals.

A Force for Good

For years, design engineer Rachel in Florida was caught in an internal conflict about how to dedicate her time, skills, and energy. There are so many problems on Earth, so many people suffering from starvation and wars. Should she spend her career playing with space technology? She agonized over her career decision for four years until concluding that it was a false dichotomy. She could do her part to take care of problems on Earth and also enjoy her life by playing with and exploring space. She volunteers and donates which gives her a good sense of balance with her day job, but she itches to do more. Despite a "healthy sort of dissatisfaction," she is happy with her job and believes in

10 Kennedy, John F. "John F. Kennedy Moon Speech." 12 September, 1962, Rice University, Houston, TX.

the mission.

Atmospheric scientist Robert in Virginia believes everything we do in space must benefit humankind. It's not enough to send something to space because it's "cool." "What we do should always be for the betterment of society, either through the acquisition of scientific knowledge or through technological innovation." Ideally, he adds, each mission we embark on must have a well-planned path with clear objectives and clear returns.

Everything we do in space must ultimately benefit society, Robert insists. We launch useful satellites. We send astronauts to better understand the space environment where our satellites operate. The earliest space exploration motivations were scientific or militaristic, but times change. Innovation drives applications and benefits in ways we can't predict, he explains.

Software manager Sarah in New Hampshire is particularly impressed with the work SpaceX and Blue Origin have done to develop reusable rocketry which she sees as less wasteful. No matter where we go, we have to keep in mind: Earth is our home. As we reach out beyond our atmosphere, we need to protect our home planet. This is where we all started. She feels Earth holds and will always hold a special place in our hearts and minds. We need to protect other planets in ways we haven't protected our own, she urges. The way she sees it, we need to begin to leave a new, more positive legacy.

Safety engineer Rachel in Florida sees the purpose of

much of the work done in LEO as improving life on Earth. Beyond Earth, human curiosity drives us to explore. Companies have an additional incentive to make a profit, she adds.

To geographer Chloe in the United Kingdom, the primary benefit of space is satellite technology. Human spaceflight is not her priority. She believes we should be investing in new satellite technologies and launch capabilities to remove barriers to market and introduce exciting new players to space. She sees increasing demand for satellite-enabled applications driving technological progress. Satellites also bring profits which she believes is paramount.

Engineer and CEO Mark in Kentucky believes there are many reasons to explore space. Close to his heart is creating a space economy. Space must be profitable for an economy to form in space and for the rate of development to accelerate, he explains.

Anne in Washington holds a somewhat contradictory view of space exploration. As a scientist, she holds as her highest belief that science and discovery are inherently beautiful and worthwhile endeavors. We humans pursue science because we can, she declares. As a pragmatist, she understands space must be sold as a business that is valued by its profit potential. She is heartened by the rise of private companies such as SpaceX which are making space travel cheaper and creating new technologies for exploring space.

Anne often wonders whether exploring space is worth the effort and resources when there are more immediate problems on Earth. Growing up in the aftermath of the September 11, 2001 attacks in the United States and the resulting wars in the Middle East, she dreams of creating a better world. In her eyes, older generations saw space exploration as the solution to major problems such as ending the Cold War, whereas many millennials see space exploration as a distraction from major problems.

Businessman Barry in Florida believes so strongly that humanity's future is in the stars, he feels the biggest risk we can take is refusing to send humans into space beyond Earth orbit at all. He is especially alarmed by the possibility of future asteroid strikes. For him, the best way to mitigate against an asteroid disaster is to understand everything we can about asteroids.

The storyteller in Barry is passionate about inspiring the next generations. Past generations, inspired by the Apollo program, coined the phrase, "If we can land a man on the Moon, why can't we…" He believes future generations will point to the work being done in space now for inspiration to do other tasks previously seen as impossible.

The businessman in Barry understands that commercial spaceflight must make a profit and create more wealth, increasing the net present value. The marginal benefit of a commercial space project must outweigh its marginal cost. Reusable rocketry, satellite applications, spinoff technologies, space resource mining, and improving the health and safety of people on Earth are just a few examples of potential profitable space ventures.

Barry even believes that sending astronauts to Mars will be profitable in the long term. “Why would you invest to create a transit system to a place where there is nothing yet there?” he asks rhetorically. “Because there is nothing there yet,” he replies. He predicts martian settlements will establish trade routes as people on Earth have done throughout human history.

The Spirit of Exploration

Human factors engineer Victor in Texas believes that at the core, efforts in space feed our innate curiosity and desire to know. He explains space is the last frontier and a vast one at that: a perfect playground for the most inquisitive explorers. All humans were born to explore, he concludes.

Humans have always been explorers, engineer Paige in California reflects. We wonder, we learn, and we are insatiably curious. She sees the same drive to explore Earth now leading us into space. Regardless of setbacks, she feels humanity will always find ways to explore the cosmos.

Mechanical engineer Tracie in Alabama believes, “The desire for exploration is embedded in our DNA.” She quotes George Mallory who attempted to reach the summit of Mount Everest, “Because it’s there.”[11] President John F. Kennedy’s speech also inspires her: “We choose to do these things not because they are easy because they are hard.” “Striving to do the ‘hard things’ is what advances society,”

---

11 “Hazards of the Alps.” *The New York Times*, 29 August 1923.

she explains. When people undertake these grand challenges, all of humanity benefits. She is excited about how much of an impact her work makes. But she doesn't believe the broader population is cognizant of how much the advanced technology in their daily lives is made possible by NASA. Everything NASA does from Earth observation to aeronautics to scientific research on the ISS benefits life on Earth, she explains.

Aerospace engineer Mason in Alabama believes most people recognize the potential of space. We've all seen a universe of spaceships in science fiction games, shows, and movies. We can grasp the scale of the possible changes to society that space exploration can provide. He believes Americans expect the United States to lead space efforts and push the boundaries of exploration, science, and technology. Companies are starting to figure out there's money to be made in space and are vigorously pursuing those profits. For so long, space has been relegated to dreams and fantasy, but in our lifetimes, these dreams are becoming reality, he exclaims. "It's the beginning of another age of exploration." The hard part, he cautions, is figuring out how to harness the potential of space into a functioning and sustainable program.

Engineer Kyle in Washington is motivated by a desire to learn new things and accomplish feats that have never been done before. Scientists seek science, explores push boundaries, and businesses can figure out how to profit on it all, he explains. He believes humans are curious people and space enables multiple ways to satisfy that curiosity.

Space has a "cool factor" that captivated mechanical engineer Chelsea in Florida even at a young age. Many kids (and adults) dream of being astronauts, she states. She points out that NASA's latest astronaut application period in 2017 received a record 18,300+ hopefuls. She believes humans are explorers. We want to know what's out there. And Americans are proud of NASA's space accomplishments. It's no secret to her friends and colleagues that Chelsea takes pride in her work.

Engineer Lindsay in Alabama believes we humans want to live and work in space out of an intrinsic need to explore. She insists we must satisfy our desire to learn as much about the world we live in as we can. The desire to learn propels technological progress, she explains. Profit and national pride are natural byproducts, she adds.

Physicist Lindsey in Maryland believes we humans have a drive to explore and discover. Space inspires and captivates great minds, she attests. Space exploration also encourages technological progress including new discoveries and spinoff technologies that move society forward and raise our quality of life, she expands. As an additional benefit, she adds, space can also be profitable for businesses and bring about a sense of national pride.

From the beginning of time, humans have been explores, and that drive to explore doesn't stop at the edge of Earth's atmosphere, safety engineer Kevin in Florida explains. He believes national pride plays a role in setting our exploration goals.

Engineer Nathan in Colorado believes we explore space to understand our origins and the nature of existence. He sees space explorers and dreamers as pursuing their own self-identification as humans in a larger Universe. Profit and technological progress may play a role as well, he adds. He believes national pride played more of a role in the early days of space exploration.

We explore space because we are curious, engineer Justin in Florida states. He believes since the end of the Cold War, national pride hasn't been the primary driver for space exploration. We go outward to explore for science. More recently, he views profit as a driver for some space users. He credits the millennial generation with the positive swing in commercial space.

Computer scientist Michael believes humans have a natural ethos to explore. And in his mind, there is no exploration opportunity grander than space. We have a natural curiosity of the unknown, he explains. Opportunity, technology, and profit are the natural side effects of this pursuit, he adds.

Engineer Nicholas in Texas believes it's human nature to explore the cosmos and the other unknowns this world has to offer. We humans enjoy challenges and discovery, he declares. To him, the questions of the Universe call out to us and we must seek the answers. Some of those answers lie beyond our planet. He's an advocate of human exploration of Mars, but more than that, he's an advocate of human exploration of whatever lies beyond.

Aerospace engineer Yasmin in Florida believes we explore space to make a difference in a field with a lot of future potential.

Space travel has the greatest potential to advance humanity technologically and socially, explains aerospace engineer Andy in Alabama. The work is tough and requires huge sacrifices, but we do it because it's important to us, he explains. He echoes President Kennedy: we do it because it's there. Andy is particularly interested in making humanity a multi-planetary species by getting humans to Mars. He hopes to see astronauts on Mars in his lifetime.

Aerospace engineer Darius in Alabama promotes the benefits of space technology: Global Positioning System (GPS), cell phones, water filtration systems, recycling processes, flame retardant fire-fighting attire, and so much more. And that's just the "side effects," he clarifies. He's also fascinated by the possibility of obtaining resources in space through processes such as asteroid mining. We may make discoveries in space that could change humanity for the better in ways we can't yet even imagine, he dreams. He insists that we have to keep looking and exploring. "Who knows what we'll find?"

Student and museum tour guide Walter in Florida advocates for appreciating the benefits of space activities in everyday life. Space has become so much a part of our everyday lives, he explains, we view it as basic as running water and electricity. As a result, utilizing space improves how we live on Earth, he adds. "It's important to keep going because who knows what will come out of it in the next 50 years."

Survival of the Species

Aviator Christopher in Florida believes space is a necessity for the very survival of the human race. He cautions that we never know when natural or human-initiated disasters will make our planet uninhabitable. While we are still living on Earth, he appreciates how much space technology benefits all of humanity with spinoff technologies in our everyday lives.

Engineer Genevieve in Texas believes space exploration is critical to human advancement and survival. By exploring, we learn so much about our planet and ourselves, she explains. Space exploration is not only outward looking but also inward looking, she elaborates, helping us to understand more about our own planet.

Communicator Brice in Alabama is passionate about space exploration as a means to ensure the survival of the human race. He believes we need to get into space to protect humanity and our ongoing culmination of thousands of years of civilization. But, he emphasizes, "it's not just about surviving; it's about thriving." The history of humanity has shown him that when we face challenges, we overcome them and come out of them better equipped to make better lives for ourselves and our descendants. To him, space is the next great challenge. The goal of space settlement provides opportunities to make life better for humans and other life on Earth, he concludes.

Ultimately, astrobiologist Joshua in California believes we need to progress in space to ensure the survival of human civilization. He reminds us that our Sun has a finite lifetime and therefore life on Earth has an expiration date. Our Sun is a G-type main sequence star, around halfway through its approximately 10-billion-year lifespan before it ceases fusing hydrogen and expands to become a red giant then collapses to form a white dwarf. Any one of a number of potential calamities could destroy a human civilization on Earth and even trigger our extinction, he warns. “If humans choose to remain on Earth, then sooner or later we will become extinct. The only way to ensure our survival is to expand human civilization into space.”

Why explore space? Aerospace engineer Logan in Alabama believes we have to. We need to ensure the long-term survival of our species. Earth will not support us forever, so humanity must learn to live off-planet, he insists. He believes humanity will only be safe once we have a few million people living in self-sustaining settlements off-Earth. We need to start working toward that goal now, he warns.

Geomorphology graduate student Stephanie in California believes we work in space to help grow humanity through distributing our population. As humans, our nature from birth is to explore, she explains. We are natural explorers. She believes space is where we are called to explore next.

Understanding the Universe

Computer engineer Joslyn in Florida sees the benefit of

space exploration to rapidly advance scientific and technological development. Exploration and trailblazing are part of the American spirit and tradition, she explains. She believes we continue to explore because it is our fundamental human nature to ponder our place in the Universe and wonder if we are alone.

Astrophysics student Xzavier in Florida believes we explore space because it is new, exciting, and challenging. "Space is like a beautiful light source and we are like curious moths that are mesmerized and eager to explore this realm."

Astronomer and astrobiologist Giada in Maryland is driven by personal curiosity and excitement about space. Space missions benefit all of humanity, she asserts, and represent major milestones in the history of our species. To her, there's something really special about being able to take a photograph of Earth from millions of miles away. She views the "Blue Marble"[12] and "Pale Blue Dot"[13] images of our planet as, "priceless gifts to all people on Earth."

Biomedical engineer Jordan in British Columbia believes we as a society travel to space for the same reason our ancestors pondered the stars thousands of years ago: curiosity. "The human curiosity to understand the world

---

12 The Blue Marble is the name of a photograph taken of Earth by the *Apollo 17* crew on December 7, 1972.

13 The Pale Blue Dot is the name of a photograph taken of Earth by *Voyager 1* on February 14, 1990 from approximately 3.7 billion miles or 6 billion kilometers away.

around us is so strong and innate that it cannot be confined to a single pale blue dot." He goes so far to say that humans have such a deep and profound sense of curiosity, we as individuals are often driven to be the first person to discover something new and show it to the world. He believes we explore space to answer the question, "Why?"

Engineer Lyndsay in Virginia believes we explore space for the sake of curiosity in the name of science, technology, and pushing the limits of humanity. Similarly, astronomer Jen in Arkansas is driven to explore the cosmos by her thirst for knowledge. She sees the utility in pursuing science for the sake of exploration and gaining knowledge.

Astronomer Rodrigo in New York believes we explore space to answer many of the "big questions" including understanding our origins and discovering whether life exist elsewhere. As a civilization, he sees us as constantly growing. That growth will inevitably lead us to expand into space, he concludes.

Geodesist Ryan in Colorado believes we perform scientific investigations beyond Earth because the public is willing to pay to know the answers to fundamental science questions: Is there life elsewhere? What makes Earth unique? What can physical processes on other planets tell us about Earth? Many of these scientific questions can be answered with robotic explorers, he admits. Despite this, "I refuse to abandon the idea that these destinations are real places that human beings can and should eventually experience directly."

Astrobiologist Eddie in California dreams of finding life elsewhere in the Universe. Is there a more compelling question in space sciences than, "Are we alone?" he ponders. This single question, "is one of the most monumental and consequential questions humanity has asked itself since we realized the points of light in the heavens were *places*, planets and stars, where we could envision life developing like it did on Earth."

Whether it's searching for present or past life on Mars, launching probes to the outer Solar System and into the seas of icy moons, or deploying large space-based telescopes that give us our first chances to find signs of life in the atmospheres of Earth-like exoplanets, Eddie believes public funding for the search for life and related sciences is essential. The answer to this fundamental question of whether life in the Universe is common or exceedingly rare could guide our view of ourselves as a species, he explains. Beyond just answering this question, he hopes for a future where we reach beyond the confines of our own world to become an interplanetary civilization.

Eddie knows he could get a bigger paycheck doing another job, but he's in it for the science and the exploration. He wishes there was more money in science to keep people in the field. "Human capital is the most important resource that the American space program has going for it, and there should be more of an active effort to sustain, grow, and nurture" it. He views technological progress, profit, and national pride as dues paid back to the society that funds scientific exploration. He is also mindful of societal factors that prevent some people from disadvantaged backgrounds from entering or staying in the field. He does his best to make sure his community is welcoming to all.

Planetary scientist Ryan in Missouri feels the call of space exploration as part of human nature. It's humans destiny to leave this planet, she believes. Her faith also motivates her. God made a beautiful Universe, so why not explore it? she asks. Understanding our home planet also motivates her. Understanding the Solar System helps us to understand Earth, she explains. The more we send humans out into the cosmos, the more we learn about ourselves and humanity, such as how our bodies and minds operate in extreme environments. She also believes space travel inspires people to accomplish big things and pursue science and engineering. The resulting technological progress betters lives on Earth, she adds. She sees national pride as still being a motivator, but international collaboration is gaining significance. She rejects the notion that space travel should be a solely profitable business.

Geology graduate student Sean in Arizona believes it's vital to allow exploration and discovery to create a paradigm shift in society. "Humans will no longer see themselves as a one planet species. We'll no longer have one data point. It will test the way we think about our planet, our lives, and our future. This shift in perspective is something I am deeply interested in."

Part of the beauty of the ISS in the mind of engineer Alex in Georgia is that many countries are able to set aside linguistic and cultural differences to further human advancement. We go to space because it excites us to accomplish anything we set our minds to and that there is no limit to human progress, he reflects. In his mind, we strive to discover the unknown and space is the new unknown.

Engineer Mark in Virginia considers himself restless. He feels called upon to push the frontier. Each time explorers push a little further, we greatly benefit as a whole. He likes to think we work towards a common goal of unity because there is no way a single nation can explore space alone.

Corporate communicator Evan in Washington, DC believes we work in space, "because that's where the boundaries end." The line that divides states, countries, and peoples on Earth aren't as relevant in space, he asserts. He believes this unbounded mindset is critical to our future as a species. In space, he sees an opportunity to work as a human civilization. It's a lofty and maybe unrealistic goal, but he is inspired by it.

My Motivations

Although the dream of people exploring the Moon was the catalyst that sparked my interest in space, many ideas have motivated me along the way. I won't repeat the many inspiring and practical reasons for space exploration our panel has so persuasively stated, but I'll add my perspective.

As a student, I wanted to understand how this beautiful creation we glimpse with telescopes came to be. As a scientist, I'm inspired by the endless scientific questions emerging from space exploration. More data seems to answer some mysteries while posing many new ones. As a space industry analyst, I understand the necessity for creating business cases to form stable markets to encourage companies, entrepreneurs, and investors to develop technologies and operate within space. As an aspiring astronaut, I want to see myself taking a trip to space someday, visiting some of those real destinations out there or even just seeing the breathtaking beauty of planet Earth from above. As a mother, I want my children to enjoy the technological advances and spaceflight opportunities envisioned by science fiction. We can make those visions become a reality with what we do today.

Boldly Going For Science, Exploration, and Survival

Millennials are motivated to explore the cosmos for many of the same reasons humanity has historically taken to the stars. Although some may disagree, most millennials believe humans have an innate sense of curiosity built into our DNA. Humans have expanded across the globe. Naturally, we'd also expand off the globe.

Many millennials are driven by their curiosity of both simple and complex questions, some of which have been asked for millennia. From the basic yet still unknown, "Are we alone?" to the ever-more-specialized questions about what we observe in the Universe. These data are especially useful when we can apply solutions to our own lives. Practical applications of our discoveries help us make the world a better place.

For some millennials, space is necessary for our very survival. No longer optional, for them we much go outward to spread our population and mitigate against planetary disaster. Note this does not equate to abandoning Earth. Instead, it requires shifting our perspective from a single-planet home to calling multiple planetary bodies home, perhaps also encompassing artificial homes in the form of space stations and deep space vehicles.

Motivations lacking for most millennials: geopolitics and national pride. Although these justifications are still strong motivators for government leaders who concern themselves with national priorities, international leadership, and geopolitical competition, they fail to ring true for most millennials who tend to have a more international outlook.

Profit is vital for the private companies who inspire millennials, but profit is not a vital motivator for millennials. If millennials are motivated by money, it is a secondary priority in space exploration and development.

Chapter 3
Our Next Steps in Human Spaceflight

Where to Boldly Go?

"It's the journey, not the destination," a popular saying goes. But to many in the space sector, the destination is key. The best next space destination for future human explorers depends on who you ask. Various motives, plans, mission architectures, and personal callings contribute to honest disagreements on the best path forward for humanity in space. If there is one. Perhaps there are many. Before NASA's Artemis program in 2019 focused NASA's attention on a human return back to – sorry, forward to – the Moon, I asked our millennial panel which destination they preferred.

The Moon

During the Apollo program, NASA astronauts landed on the Moon six times between 1969 and 1972. And to the chagrin of many, humans have not returned to the Moon since. Astronauts have barely explored the Moon's 14.6 million square miles or 38 million square kilometers of the lunar surface, an area larger than Africa.

Many justifications are given for returning astronauts to the Moon including scientific, business, geopolitical, and exploratory. Since those initial Apollo visits, scientists have discovered the presence of water ice on the Moon as well as other potentially useful minerals. The Moon also holds clues to scientific questions such as the formation of the Earth-Moon system and the creation of its many craters. At an average of "only" 238,855 miles or 384,402 kilometers from Earth, the Moon is the closest planetary body to us, minimizing travel time through the harmful microgravity and radiation environment of space. It helps motivate some to know that many nations, both allies and adversaries, also plan to send crewed missions to the Moon.

Aerospace engineer Eric in Alabama sees the logic in a tiered approach to human spaceflight: first LEO, then the Moon, then Mars. We use each destination to prepare to go beyond. With humans living and working in LEO on the ISS continuously since 2000, he believes we are ready to go beyond.

Engineer Mark in Virginia has a vision of dry docks and processing stations in LEO. These outpost would help open the frontier to the inner Solar System. He would also like to see humans push out to the Moon and Mars, two celestial bodies that hold great promise for science and technology development. He imagines these two neighbors being our way stations to the outer Solar System.

Aerospace engineer Christopher in Colorado hopes humans return to the Moon and establish a permanent presence there similar to the ISS. There is still so much we don't know about the Moon. He believes such missions would provide a great learning environment to test new technologies that could one day take humans to other planets.

Biologist David in California has his sights set on the Moon. We have to go back, he insist. "It's too close and too obvious of a training ground to ignore" if we want to eventually send humans to Mars. He hopes NASA returns to the lunar surface with more scientists next time. Due to fiscal constraints and a broader portfolio of programs and projects, he understands NASA needs to progress more incrementally than they did during the Apollo program.

Planetary scientist Ryan in Missouri is looking forward to humans traveling beyond LEO and back to the lunar surface. In fact, returning to the Moon before venturing out to asteroids or Mars is imperative to her. She supports an incremental approach to human exploration. She believes humans need to learn to live and work for extended periods of time on the harsh environment of the Moon so we can address many questions while still being within a safe distance of Earth.

Engineer Justin in Florida supports a human mission to the Moon as the most reasonable next destination because of the resources the Moon has to offer and because of the relative ease of getting there. He envisions astronauts building a sustainable human habit on the Moon. He believes it's safer and smarter to send astronauts to a closer planetary body such as the Moon where we can resupply and communicate with fewer difficulties than a farther destination.

Software manager Sarah in New Hampshire believes we have so much out there to explore beyond the usual destinations. That's not to say she isn't excited about these nearby planetary bodies where we may send humans in the near future. She believes we should return to the Moon next as a closer and safer destination than Mars. But there will always be risk and danger, she warns, and we don't know what we don't know. We can try to make missions as safe as possible but she knows we cannot guard against every risk, especially if we don't know what those unknown risks are.

Biology student Skye in Florida envisions humanity traveling to the Moon to test our space exploration technology before traveling on to Mars. Mars is dangerous. She believes we need to ensure that our technology and our mission operations are suitable and we can fix anything that needs fixing before we travel farther from our planet than we ever have before. "If we try to go to Mars before testing the water on another destination we know is reliable, we may be stepping into potentially very dangerous waters."

Distance to various geographical locations on Earth isn't a barrier for engineer Nicholas in Washington. And neither is the distance to the Moon. At least, it's not a barrier we can't and won't overcome, he insists. He envisions a future in which not only are people connected on this planet but on other planets as well. Moon bases are just the beginning for him. He foresees people traveling to our closest planetary neighbor with sustainable rocketry and permanent settlements. He hopes lunar resources and the challenges of the harsh environment will spur technological innovation. The Moon would then become a rallying point for deeper missions reaching out farther into the Universe, he conjectures, first to Mars, then as far as we can go.

Engineer and businessman Dan in Pennsylvania believes the Moon should be a priority for human spaceflight. The techniques and technologies needed to operate beyond Earth orbit for long-duration spaceflight should be demonstrated in cislunar space, the space between the Earth and the Moon, before going on to expensive and challenging farther destinations, he explains. No matter the destination, he wants to see a sustainable human spaceflight program that incrementally unlocks new capabilities and permanently moves forward the frontier of exploration. He believes it would be wise to seek progress toward Earth-independent human spaceflight architectures.

Engineer Hayley in California wants to see astronauts back on the Moon. She has a wild idea to capture an asteroid and move it to Earth's gravitational field to orbit as a new moon. She believes it's important to pursue ISRU technologies to learn to build on other celestial surfaces using local materials and to become less reliant on Earth's resources.

Moon to Mars

Geology graduate student Sean in Arizona supports a Moon-to-Mars concept for humans in space exploration. As humanity explores, he believes it's important we travel beyond the cradle and embark upon the next frontier. He thinks it's time we view the settlement of space not as science fiction but as a pragmatic survivalist strategy. He hopes to see astronauts return to the Moon and establish a base there to learn to live off-planet. Then we'll be ready to travel to Mars to establish an environment there.

Astrophysics student Xzavier in Florida supports establishing a Moon base where astronauts can learn to live on another planetary body before going on to Mars. If we can learn to survive on the Moon, we will be ready for Mars, he explains.

Aerospace engineer Yasmin in Florida believes it would be wise to first build a lunar base before tackling a human mission to Mars. Experimenting with a lunar base would help us gain confidence in reaching a farther distance, she explains. On the Moon, she foresees astronauts learning to live on another gravitational body other than Earth before going onto Mars.

Engineer Lyndsay in Virginia supports continuing to improve space exploration technologies to safely maintain a human presence on the Moon. She believes Mars is the next reasonable step after lunar ventures. To her, spacecraft safety, spacecraft longevity, and life support systems will determine how fit we are to explore deep-space destinations such as Mars. We should keep practicing and developing on the Moon, she advises. She supports pushing boundaries in pursuit of new space destinations.

CEO Scott in Florida supports humans settling on the Moon before trying to settle Mars. He doesn't believe we have the proper technology yet to protect humans from the space radiation astronauts will be exposed to on the way to Mars and back, not to mention the martian surface if habitats aren't shielded. He also worries about bone density loss and other physiological problems during a long journey to Mars. And what if crops fail during the long trip? He believes the most important step now is to prove we can live on the Moon for extended periods of time before we make the long journey to the red planet.

Moon first, then Mars, believes science educator John in Florida. The Moon is a platform to test technologies that will benefit travel to Mars such as habitation modules, agriculture, propulsion systems, and radiation testing. He believes NASA and the private space sector should have a strong foothold in Earth orbit and the Moon before traveling beyond.

To space policy professional Nate in Washington, D.C., exploring "beyond LEO" means humans to the Moon and ultimately to Mars. He foresees human exploration of the Moon as being an international effort where we can test out how to live and operate on another world without being too far from home if something goes wrong. An astronaut journey to Venus has also captured his imagination. Our closest planetary neighbor in the opposite direction[14] often gets overlooked because of its thick, hot, toxic atmosphere, but could be an innovative target for human exploration.

Student and museum tour guide Walter in Florida believes we should send astronauts to the Moon followed by Mars in a sustainable, permanent way. The Moon has opportunities for exploration and exploitation. He imagines we could build up the Moon to create a giant solar power plant. "Mars has been a target for human exploration for a few decades now," and he believes the most likely candidate to support a human settlement in the inner Solar System. He hopes a future Mars settlement will be an ongoing mission.

Humans are fascinating, and nothing fascinates busi-

---

14 Technically, Mercury is the closest neighbor to Earth on average than any other planet thanks to its short orbit around the Sun. It's difficult to explain, so I encourage you to look up some great animations showing why Mercury is closest on average to Earth. But in terms of how we usually think of the order of planets by distance from the Sun, Venus is next to Earth.

ness consultant Liam in Virginia more than the renewed push for human planetary exploration. Mars is thrilling, but Liam has other priorities: returning astronauts to the Moon. There's too much work still to be done by lunar astronauts, we've hardly scratched the surface, he explains. He envisions lunar surface experiments and cislunar stations for scientific study and technological progress. Continuing a human presence in Earth orbit is equally as valuable to him for the same reasons. He hopes to live to see space habitats become more affordable for the average person.

Mars has the cool factor. A human mission to Mars is an immense project and a power symbol, Liam explains. He prioritizes missions closer to home, but he can't deny the human draw to Mars. He hopes millennials will step foot on Mars before their time is through. His dedication to these missions is so strong, he believes the missions will outlive him.

The Call of the Red Planet

There is no denying the "cool factor" of Mars. Mars captures many people's imagination. Some go as far as to dismiss a return to the Moon entirely, preferring to send astronauts directly to Mars. "We've been there before," snubbed President Barack Obama[15] when he shifted NASA's direction away from the Constellation Program's Moon-to-Mars focus in 2010. In an infamous tweet, Presi-

---

15 Obama, Barack. "President Barack Obama on Space Exploration in the 21st Century." 15 April, 2010, John F. Kennedy Space Center, Merritt Island, FL.

dent Donald Trump advised NASA leadership, "NASA should NOT be talking about going to the Moon - We did that 50 years ago. They should be focused on the much bigger things we are doing, including Mars..."[16] President Trump's point: the American public is more enthusiastic about astronauts on Mars than they are about astronauts on the Moon.

There are challenges to overcome when sending astronauts to a distant planet where no person has ever stepped foot before. The distance is farther: a minimum distance of 33.9 million miles or 54.6 million kilometers, more than 100 times farther away than the Moon. A farther travel distance increases the biological, psychological, and technical dangers to astronauts and their life-supporting home-away-from-home spacecraft. And that's just getting there; landing and exploring have their own challenges. Many of the technologies developed for the ISS and lunar exploration can be used for martian exploration, but Mars has a unique environment with its own requirements and challenges.

Mars also has benefits. Mars' average surface gravity is 0.376 g or approximately 38% of Earth's gravity of 1 g. Compare that to the Moon's smaller average surface gravity of 0.166 g or approximately 17% of Earth's gravity. The length of a martian day is approximately the same as on Earth, 24 hours and 37 minutes. A lunar day is much longer, almost month: 29 days, 12 hours, and 44 minutes. Mars also has a thin atmosphere and water ice caps mixed with

---

16 @realDonaldTrump (Donald Trump), *Twitter*, 7 July, 2019

CO_2 (dry ice) at its poles. Mars has long captured humanity's imagination in science fiction from a misunderstanding of astronomer Percival Lowell's martian *canali* (meaning channels but mistranslated as canals) in 1895 to present day big-budget films.

Engineer Vito in Colorado supports a human mission to the Moon, which is right there in our own backyard. But his true goal is sending humans to Mars for one simple reason: we have not yet done so. Mars is a diverse world with ice, dust storms, geological diversity, and an atmosphere, he adds. "We have been on [Wernher] von Braun's journey to Mars for 70 years, but we need to complete a new milestone soon."

Human factors engineer Victor in Texas has his heart set on Mars. A human mission to Mars is long overdue, he insists. He understands that the next logical step in human space exploration is to establish a lunar base. Working on the Moon could provide basic practice for constructing habitats. And even more importantly to Victor, a lunar base could provide insight into the human factors of living in a real, isolated space habitat. However, he warns that these efforts should not distract or hinder a human mission to Mars. He will do anything he can to help further our journey on our road to Mars.

Geomorphology graduate student Stephanie in California understands that sending astronauts to the Moon is the better choice logistically. However, she believes Mars would be a better next destination. Visiting Mars would keep the public's interest up and thereby keep the funding alive. She concedes visiting the Moon would allow for faster technological growth because of the shorter trip.

Satellite engineer Adam in Colorado foresees exciting collaborations between government and commercial partners such as long-term missions to other planets including Mars. Especially Mars. The red planet is his destination of choice. It's the next logical step for human exploration after the Moon, he asserts. He is particularly interested in the potential of past or maybe even present life on Mars.

Aerospace engineer Kelly in Florida believes since we have already sent astronauts to the Moon, our next challenge should be Mars. Once we understand how to use the martian resources, we can use Mars as a gateway to the rest of our Solar System, she explains. But more important to her than simply planting a flag is establishing a sustained human presence there.

Safety engineer Rachel in Florida believes Mars is the next logical destination for humans. Of all the planets in the Solar System, Mars is closest to Earth in terms of temperature and available resources such as water. It doesn't matter to her whether NASA or the private industry sets foot on Mars first; either way it's an achievement for the entire human race.

Considering his love of Mars rover *Curiosity*, it's no surprise astronomer Brett in Queensland believes humans should visit Mars next. Mars is an appealing destinations to him as the most similar planet to Earth in our Solar System with a thin atmosphere, frozen water, and other useful resources. However, he admits it's a tough destination with a high radiation environment and long mission durations. Such an ambitious mission will undoubtedly lead to technological breakthroughs that will benefit society, he explains.

Engineer Alex in Georgia has his sights on Mars. With new discoveries of water on Mars and some geophysical similarities with Earth, he thinks the red planet is where humanity should go next. However, NASA's budget needs to increase substantially to achieve a human expedition to Mars, he explains. Half of 1% of the national budget isn't going to cut it, he insists. NASA's fiscal year 2019 budget was $21.9 billion representing 0.49% of the U.S. federal budget.

Businessman Barry in Florida has his heart set on Mars. He doesn't mind human space exploration missions with other purposes – asteroids, cislunar space, lunar orbit, the lunar surface – so long as the goal is to get humans to Mars. Truly, he wants it all. Give NASA as much funding as it needs to make it all happen, he says, as much money as is needed for an Apollo-sized mission and then some. He believes a sustained human presence on Mars is the only way to make the immense expense of such a mission worth it.

Although not a scientist himself, Barry is fascinated by what we could learn on Mars. What happened to all the water? Could Earth someday become dry? Has microbial life ever inhabited Mars, and if so, where did it come from and is it still there? He doesn't believe robotic exploration will ever be able to answer these vital questions, so we must send humans to unlock these mysteries.

Astronomer Rodrigo in New York believes Mars holds the answers to some of the most important questions we can ask. There's plenty of evidence that Mars could have been habitable in the past, he states. He is curious: Did life ever envolve on the red planet? If so what happened to it? If not why not? Could there still be life on Mars, perhaps safely hidden in the subsurface, that is, underground?

The technology is almost there to get humans to Mars, Rodrigo asserts. If we are really set on sending astronauts there, he estimates we could do so in the next couple decades. Companies such as SpaceX and Blue Origin have shown that private money can go a long way toward enabling human space exploration. With the backing of private investors and the support of the public, he believes we may not need the level of government funding that NASA had in the 1960s during the Apollo program to send humans to Mars. At its peak between 1964 and 1966, NASA's budget was approximately 4% of the U.S. federal budget. He believes we may be able to send humans to Mars for less funding than what NASA spent during the Apollo program.

For engineer Tom in Florida, Mars is the ultimate goal. By studying the mysteries of the red planet, we can learn science applicable to our own planet such as how the martian environment and climate evolved into the barren world we see today. Learning as much as we can about the atmospheres and geological processes of other planets directly benefits the scientific advances on Earth.

Astrobiologist Eddie in California envisions a Mars civilization. He sees Mars as the ultimate great destination because of the likelihood of a permanent human habitation. ISRU is a great way to build a civilization from the ground up, literally, he declares. He believes the cornucopia of useful raw materials on the martian surface and the thin martian atmosphere could provide useful building blocks for establishing a settlement on Mars. This endeavor would be more difficult than any other challenge humans have ever faced while exploring regions of our own planet, he cautions. There's a greater chance of living off the land in even the most remote and extreme destinations on Earth than there is anywhere else in the Universe that we know. He imagines the martian land might harbor fossils or other evidence of ancient life. But even Mars is more accessible than the outer Solar System filled with fascinating worlds so far from our grasp, he explains.

To Eddie, the exact answer to *where* humans go is less important than *how* humans go, or more specifically, *how long* humans go. He believes human spaceflight goals should be designed to maximize the opportunity for sustained and continued exploration and investment in space technologies to facilitate a permanent and growing human presence in space beyond Earth. He thinks an impressive, ambitious human mission to Mars could generate the excitement to marshal public support for the endeavor. But just as the Apollo missions were ultimately canceled, a one-off dash toward a new Solar System locale could easily be abandoned after the fact. He would rather humanity stay. Human spaceflight is risky but he believes some risk is always necessary to achieve daring goals.

Corporate communicator Evan in Washington, DC would like to see humans return to Mars. He believes the technical challenges of such a mission will yield technologies we can use on future missions to go even farther into space. Human spaceflight is the future for our species, he predicts.

Safety engineer Kevin in Florida believes Mars is the next logical step for human exploration. A human mission to Mars would require technology advancements in areas such as propulsion systems and long-term life support. He concludes we are not too far off from a day when such an ambitious mission to the red planet can become a reality. But he doesn't believe we should aim for a "mission accomplished" symbolic objective. If our goal is to explore and potentially inhabit other worlds, then it needs to be done incrementally and wisely, he advises.

Biomedical engineer Jordan in British Columbia believes Mars is the best goal for human space exploration to inspire young lives, drive technological innovation, and focus everyone on a singular goal to advance humanity to a new frontier.

Engineer Paige in California wants NASA to jump on the current public excitement surrounding a human mission to Mars. The red planet has a relatively friendly environment compared to other destinations in our Solar System, she explains. Martian mysteries call out to us, she imagines, beckoning us to explore them first-hand. And most importantly in her mind, astronauts on Mars could boost public support for space. She imagines a NASA-led human mission to Mars would be bipartisan and international. Furthermore, she dreams, such a mission may create a sense of unity that is currently lacking in the United States and the greater global community. She believes space exploration has many such secondary benefits to people on Earth.

Engineer Nathan in Colorado believes future settlements on Mars would capture the public attention with wonder. He anticipates people living on Mars would inspire the next generation to get involved. These settlements could, "give people a sense of pride in humanity," and, "bring people together in a particular way that few other achievements can."

Physicist Lindsey in Maryland is most excited about sending humans to Mars because such a mission would capture public attention and excitement, she describes. However, we need to better understand the challenges of long-duration spaceflight to Mars, she explains. She believes NASA's goal should be to dare, to stretch the limits of our capabilities.

Atmospheric scientist Robert in Virginia is skeptical that current technology is enough to progress humanity to where we want to go. Rocket reusability interests him, but he doesn't believe the cost of spaceflight will ever decline significantly with today's chemical rocket propulsion. Human missions to Mars may produce great science, he admits, but we need to solve the radiation problem first. He is intrigued by the idea of generational interstellar ships as well. But without a clear benefit to society, he believes such missions would be impractical.

Astrobiologist Joshua in California has his sights on Mars, the planet he believes is most conducive to long-term human habitation than anywhere else in our Solar System except Earth. The scientific returns from sending humans to Mars would be great, he forecasts, greater than anywhere else we could realistically set up camp in the immediate future. He believes human missions to other destinations such as the Moon, asteroids, and Lagrangian points could be stepping stones to test technology on the way to Mars.

Engineer Genevieve in Texas supports a human mission to Mars with possible visits to an asteroid or one of the two martian moons Phobos and Deimos first. She would welcome another burst of funding for space exploration, the kind of budget increase last seen in the Apollo era. But she understands today's space policy only supports an incremental approach to space exploration.

Astronomer Crystal in Maryland would like to see humans visit Mars to advance human space travel over greater distances. She's also looking beyond Mars to destinations such as Europa which may have an environment conducive for life to exist. Exploring beyond would really test our limits for space travel, she points out.

Not So Far

Not everyone has their hearts set on the Moon or Mars or thinks those worlds are the best next destination for human voyagers. Some believe humans should stick closer to home. Since the Soviet Union's *Salyut 1* in 1971, humans have been living and working on space stations in LEO.

NASA launched its first space station *Skylab* in 1973. Space stations have continued to advance with Russia's *Mir*, China's *Tiangong* program, and the ISS. Commercial companies have plans to build crewed space stations for research and tourism. With decades of experience learning to adapt to microgravity and improve space systems, some believe humanity is ready to go beyond. Others believe we still have much to learn right here in Earth orbit.

Software engineer Brandon in Washington admits he's conservative when it comes to human spaceflight. He'd prefer humanity stay in LEO for a while longer to iterate on previous and current space station technologies. The current ISS systems would not survive a trip to Mars, he explains. So it makes sense to him to take the time we are spending close to home to truly learn how to live in space.

Bioengineer Diana in California would like to see a fleet of space stations developed and operational around multiple planetary bodies and at Lagrangian points. Given how expensive it is to launch people and payloads to and from gravitational bodies, it makes more sense to her to develop settlements in space. Focusing on long-term space habitats also allows us to be more careful not to accidentally contaminate pristine extraterrestrial worlds with life from Earth, a concept known as planetary protection.

As an engineer, Alex in Alabama sees a need to build up space infrastructure. Scientific missions have the benefit of long timescales, but infrastructure development should take five years or less, he explains. However, space designs should be made with a long-term vision in mind. Incremental progress is the way to go, he adds.

Aiming for Asteroids

Under President Barack Obama, NASA developed the Asteroid Redirect Mission (ARM). Robots and humans would travel to, study, and move a nearby asteroid. Near-Earth asteroids pose a danger to our planet. ARM was designed to advance technology for planetary defense as well as better our scientific understanding of asteroids. ARM was canceled by President Donald Trump, but some still believe it's a worthwhile mission.

Aerospace engineer Brad in Colorado fondly recalls NASA's previous goal of ARM. For him, such a mission could answer key questions such as where liquid water came from, how life began on Earth, and even how we could avoid a catastrophic collision in the future. Despite the change in NASA's direction toward lunar and martian exploration, he believes humans will visit an asteroid within his lifetime.

Aerospace engineer Darius in Alabama enjoys imagining the challenge of potentially sending humans to a large asteroid someday. He sees an asteroid mission as a technological bridge between the "baby step" of sending astronauts to the Moon and the significant challenge of sending astronauts to Mars with its atmosphere and larger gravitational pull. The solutions developed to send humans to an asteroid would provide useful technology to benefit those on Earth as well as in space, he adds. We can't explore space for symbolic reasons as we did during the Cold War, he cautions; we need scientific reasoning behind our exploration.

Beyond

For some, a human mission to Mars isn't ambitious enough. Computer engineer Joslyn in Florida proposes a human mission beyond the asteroid belt, the region of space between the orbits of Mars and Jupiter. She believes the new perspective and bolder mission would energize public support for the space program. Such a long, complex mission would require more cooperation between public and private entities and international partners, she explains. She expects stimulating interest in space will inspire the future space workforce, politicians, the general public, and investors.

For some in the space sector, where humans go does not matter. Any destination is as good as the next. What matters is that we go.

Mechanical engineer Tracie in Alabama jokes taking sides in the, "Which space destination should astronauts go next?" debate is controversial, akin to talking about religion. Everyone has their own set of beliefs and are unlikely to sway anyone else's opinion, she clarifies. "I tend to focus less on destination and more on the capabilities we'll need to develop that are destination-agnostic."

Given the time and budget, engineer and space policy professional Jane believes humans can travel anywhere, even to destinations that some currently dismiss as too dangerous. Her favorite location of choice: "anywhere and everywhere." Although she admits traveling too close to the Sun might be a limitation. She envisions multi-generational missions after we learn more about the anatomical and biological effects of long-term space travel.

Then Again...

Some in the space sector aren't sure humanity is ready to leave our nest yet. Their argument is we haven't been the best stewards of the planet we have access to already. Perhaps we need more time to progress to prove we can care for our own planet before leaving our mark on currently untouched worlds.

Despite her enthusiasm for space achievements, science reporter Leah in Massachusetts doesn't believe humans belong on other planets long-term given the destructiveness of human history. She looks around planet Earth and laments where humans have exploited and damaged our natural environment. Why should we assume humans would take any better care of another planet when we treat our own home with such little care? she asks. If we do have a sustained human presence on other planets, she isn't sure that outcome will be positive for the natural environments of those currently pristine worlds. Even the very act of landing humans on the surface of these planetary bodies would irreparably contaminate currently untouched environments, harming or even preventing some scientific studies and the search for extraterrestrial life.

Where I'd Go

Given my childhood inspiration, it's no surprise I'm a "Moon first" advocate. While I do believe the Moon is a useful stepping stone to the rest of our Solar System and beyond, I also uphold the Moon as an inherently valuable destination by itself. I understand the allure of Mars and hope we send astronauts on martian missions in my lifetime. I accept the need to balance human exploration with planetary protection guidelines to help us continue to seek out life beyond our own home. However, there's no denying the spirit of exploration built into humanity – we will go out into the unknown. There's no stopping us now.

Our Dream Destinations

Millennials have lofty goals and high expectations. For many, NASA, ESA, and others are on the right track. Whether the Moon is their destination of choice or just a useful steppingstone to places beyond, most millennials agree astronauts should return to the Moon, this time to stay. We have much to learn on the lunar surface both about the Moon and about ourselves.

No destination calls to millennials the way Mars does. Almost universally, human missions to Mars is the most important goal for millennials. Just as the previous generations dreamed of traveling to the red planet, so do millennials. Whether it's a government program or a private company such as SpaceX, millennials assume a future on Mars.

For some millennials, we're just not ready yet. Whether

it's concerns over technology maturation or humanity's maturation, some would prefer we stick closer to home until we grow a bit more before venturing beyond.

Chapter 4
The Way Forward

How We Go

Just as controversial as where humans should travel next in space is how the mission should be structured. The *Apollo 11* lunar landing was one of the greatest technological achievements in human history. As a large government-funded, timeline-driven program, NASA's budget grew and NASA's employees and contractors rallied around the cause of sending astronauts to the Moon, but it was a product of its time with an impetus and budget not seen since. Arguably, it was never meant to be sustainable, financially or politically. As great a triumph as Apollo was, the final three planned Apollo missions (18, 19, and 20) were canceled, and NASA's efforts soon turned to its space station program, abandoning the Moon.

Another approach is what I'm calling incremental: slow, sustained, step-by-step (did I mention slow?). For some, despite the many successes and benefits of the ISS and previous space station programs, there is a tedium to traveling around and around Earth without traveling farther out into space. Decades of living and working in microgravity have provided valuable data and technological improvements to carry beyond LEO when we're finally ready to do so. Activity in Earth orbit is increasingly becoming commercialized with private companies taking over what has traditionally been a government domain. In theory, this transition will free government agencies to conduct new, groundbreaking missions outside of Earth such as a return to the Moon, this time to stay.

I asked our millennial panel which approach they thought is the way to go for a future mission to their favorite next destination: a huge push forward with a "flags and footprints" finish, or a more deliberately paced incremental path forward. These approaches are not mutually exclusive nor are they polar opposites. I've simplified the many complexities to kindle the conversation and let the panelists expand on the elements they viewed as most important.

Apollo Aspirations

Engineer Mark in Virginia would support an Apollo-like approach to future space exploration. Humans are meant to be challenged by the frontier, he declares. He insists it's time we stopped sitting idly on our planet.

Why wait? Engineer Paige in California emphasizes the need to act quickly so long as safety remains a top priority. Groundbreaking missions such as sending humans to Mars should take to the skies as soon as possible to maintain public support and internal motivation. She points to the Apollo program, a groundbreaking mission that failed to maintain public support and was canceled with no immediate successor. "I think any space program today needs to be thinking not only of reaching a destination, but also what steps they're going to take after that, so we don't see another decline in interest (and funding) like we saw when the Space Race died down."

Engineer and CEO Mark in Kentucky supports an ambitious, fast-moving human spaceflight mission that captures public imagination but is also sustainable. He hopes these factors are not mutually exclusive, but he admits they may be.

The best way to meet our goals, according to aerospace engineer Andy in Alabama, is a new Apollo-like mission. He has been disappointed with the lack of progress with the current incremental approach. He believes the slow pace is a huge risk to the advancement of space. Accomplishing goals too slowly causes support for the space program to dwindle, he explains.

Regardless of where humans go in space, aerospace engineer Brad would love to see another Apollo-like mission. In his eyes, it has been far too long since humans have taken any great strides in space exploration. He believes planting a flag on a new surface in the Solar System would reinvigorate public interest in space.

Astronomer Crystal in Maryland would like to see an all-out approach to space exploration such as the hugely successful Apollo missions. She believes such a grand mission would encourage public interest in space.

Engineer and CEO Jay in Alabama supports an Apollo-like mission to a space destination to inspire the people back home. "Apollo inspired generations of inventors, artists, engineers, business leaders, and a lot of others, which is invaluable." Whatever the end goal and whichever the approach, he advises, we need to commit. "Indecisiveness is our worst nightmare."

Astrobiologist Joshua in California admits that the current NASA budget is holding them back. He knows NASA will never get a budget as large as it had during the peak of the Apollo program (4.41% of the total federal budget), so he advocates doubling the current budget of approximately 0.5% to 1%. He hopes that kind of funding influx would allow for sustained human settlements on Mars.

Aerospace engineer Floyd in Iowa believes sending humans to Mars is a worthy goal. But he is skeptical of the economics of such missions given the current state of our technology and what is needed for such a novel mission. What NASA needs, he thinks, is an Apollo-style mission to Mars with its romance and national prestige. Such missions do wonders to facilitate foreign relations and promote government spending in space and technology, he adds.

Future life on Mars is what satellite engineer Adam in Colorado dreams of. He believes the millennial generation will not only set foot on Mars but will set up a permanent presence there. He approves of an Apollo-like mission that would spread inspiration across the globe, internationally. He imagines that if we as a planet could come together to establish a permanent human presence on Mars, it could offer a new opportunity for global peace and cooperation.

Step By Step

Biomedical engineer Jordan in British Columbia would like to see an initiative to send humans to Mars reminiscent of the Apollo era. He is inspired by the "romance" associated with the 1960s Space Race.

But Jordan believes the effort to send humans to Mars will be incremental. The technological, financial, and labor resources required are exponentially greater to travel to Mars than to the Moon. He envisions that the first martian missions will test long-term human endurance while traveling to and orbiting around Mars, then come back home. "I would be quite surprised if the first craft to land on Mars is a crewed by citizens of only one nation." The first landing crew will be international, he predicts, planting the flag of multiple nations on the martian surface, assuming it's appropriate to plant a national flag at all. "My prediction is that we will either be putting flags of several nations, or a single flag to represent all people and all nations of Earth."

Science reporter Leah in Massachusetts has a passion for drumming up enthusiasm for space. She believes human missions are important for that goal. Symbolic flag-planting missions are an influential first step toward building interest, funding, and the scientific knowledge necessary for successful longer term missions, she adds.

To accomplish our human spaceflight goals, corporate communicator Evan in Washington, DC supports an incremental approach. While he appreciates the Apollo program, he believes we now need a new mission that leaves us with more than, "a stack of photos, a sack of Moon rocks, and an inflated sense of nationalism." What he sees missing in NASA's current human spaceflight program is an end goal beyond just getting there. Do we sustain a permanent settlement or research base? Are we searching for extraterrestrial life? Are we setting up a second home for humanity? To him, these questions aren't yet being answered in a meaningful way.

However, Evan knows there are downsides to an incremental approach. Take NASA's canceled asteroid initiative ARM. With the changing tides of the political administration, incremental missions such as ARM can spend millions of dollars only to be canceled a few years down the line. The advantage of an Apollo-like mission with a massive budget, he believes, would be that NASA can more or less have guaranteed funding and may waste less time and money along the way. He advises a major change to NASA's funding approach as its goals get loftier and achieving them takes longer.

The public loves a good story: a hero going up against all odds. That's how engineer Kyle in Washington views the Space Race of the 1960s. But a good story alone is not going to create a sustainable approach to long-term space exploration, he insists. To truly establish a permanent human presence in the Solar System, he believes we need a strategic effort with the infrastructure and funding to make it sustainable.

Geopolitics have changed since the Cold War, space policy professional Nate in Washington, DC points out. Planting flags on a new world for national prestige was a primary goal in those days, he notes. But if we want to make progress, he insists that we need to have a comprehensive, incremental approach with resources dedicated to it. He believes follow-through is crucial for as long as it takes to make sustainable progress.

Mechanical engineer Tracie in Alabama prefers an incremental approach to human spaceflight. She'd like to see astronauts living off-world sustainably. To her, that's more meaningful to advancing science and exploration. Flag-planting missions are historically reactive and driven by nationalism, she explains. She doesn't believe those kinds of missions are sustainable in today's environment.

Astronomer and astrobiologist Giada in Maryland interprets the Apollo-era "flag planting" approach to human spaceflight as, "a surefire way to have a space program sputter and die." She prefers an incremental approach to plant the seeds for a future sustainable space program.

Geology graduate student Gabe in Arizona supports a well-thought-out incremental approach to human spaceflight backed by more genuine motivations than the geopolitical instability of the Cold War. He believes we should begin interplanetary operations first in cislunar space to tackle radiation exposure issues and hone our hardware and operational capabilities. In his judgment, this approach should reduce the risk to further human missions to asteroids or Mars. Success in this area will build public confidence and interest, he concludes.

Aerospace engineer Anthony in California sees a human mission to Mars as another way to reinvigorate public interest in space. An incremental buildup with many other smaller projects along the way is the best way to sustain such a mission, he believes. Public interest faded quickly after the success of the Apollo missions, and in his view, the space program diminished as a result. He knows an incremental approach would take longer but would allow for more opportunities along the way.

While aerospace engineer Logan in Alabama believes baby-step human missions to the Moon would increase the chance of success for human deep-space exploration, his heart is set on Mars. Going straight to Mars is more exciting and politically attractive, he explains, but he doesn't support a flag-planting mission. "One of the biggest downsides of planting a 'mission accomplished' flag is that interest drops off sharply after, with budget likely dropping as well." He regrets that Werner von Braun did not live to see his vision of permanent space stations and martian settlements. Logan would love to see von Braun's dream of a permanent space presence become a reality.

Geodesist Ryan in Colorado likens the exploration of space to the exploration of Antarctica. Like many bodies in the Solar System, he explains, Antarctica is completely inhospitable with scarce natural resources beyond water and sunlight. Initial exploration of Antarctica was an incremental process partially driven by competition towards well-defined goals, he expounds, goals such as reaching the geographic South Pole. Some expeditions were simply to pre-supply future explorers on their way to a destination. Later, a permanent outpost was constructed for scientific research. Today, Antarctica's permanent outpost houses up to 1,000 researchers and support staff from various nations.

Ryan views space exploration similarly. "We should push the limits of technology and human endurance to accomplish well-defined objectives, such as walking on Mars or nearby asteroids, and then follow those pioneer efforts with more measured approaches to construct and settle permanent outposts in the solar system."

Scientist Amy in Virginia is a fan of the incremental approach, establishing a sustained lunar base similar to the long-term presence on the ISS, then onward to Mars and farther. She believes it would be valuable to conduct shorter missions closer to home and to understand the psychological and physiological aspects of longer-term human spaceflight.

With her science background, engineering student Amoree in Georgia envisions long-term human spaceflight missions with incremental steps to allow plenty of time to conduct experiments. Smaller milestones and accomplishments add value to the overall mission, she explains. Earth and the surrounding cosmological bodies are ancient with lifespans of billions of years, so the longer the mission, the longer we short-lived humans can obtain accurate data, she reasons.

CEO Scott in Florida supports an incremental approach to sustaining a human presence in space. If we follow an Apollo-like approach, he warns, we will potentially spend billions of dollars to travel to only one destination. Technology would then need to innovate and evolve for the next new destination with different requirements, he adds. However, if we take an incremental approach, he believes we will create the option to develop systems and tools to explore multiple destinations.

Astrophysicist Jacob in the United Kingdom supports an incremental approach to human spaceflight. First thing's first, he says, a return to the Moon – a great accomplishment! Then on to Mars. He believes he will see the first human mission to Mars before he retires.

Communicator Brice in Alabama looks back at the past few decades and notes how inconsistent funding and clashing ideals have made it difficult to implement long-term space exploration plans. He prefers an incremental approach to maximize the possibility of permanently bringing humans into space. He's not necessarily a "Moon first" advocate, but he views a lunar or cislunar mission as more likely to be sustainable. He sees hope in both government and private space efforts taking steps to develop a sustainable, expanding human presence in space.

Being more internationally-focused, it's no surprise engineer and data scientist Nikolai in the Czech Republic isn't fond of the "flags and footprints" model of space exploration. He doesn't see planting a flag then moving on as an achievement. His goal is to move beyond politically motivated space missions, move beyond what we have done with the ISS, and move beyond temporary space habitats. Even living on the surfaces of hostile planetary bodies subject to radiation and gravity deficiencies doesn't appeal to him. He has a wild idea to hollow out an asteroid, spin it to create a centrifugal force equivalent to Earth's gravity 1 g, and set up a permanent human habitat inside, protected from harm.

Computer scientist Michael advocates for an incremental, long-term approach for expanding humanity into space. He foresees our systems of government iterating and our economies expanding once we become multi-planetary.

Nicholas in Texas believes incremental steps are key. As an engineer, he knows nothing goes 100% right the first time and there are always kinks to be ironed out. Incremental progress can improve reliability and safety, he explains. He takes risks and safety very seriously. Safety is always a top priority in his mind, driving risk down to as close to zero as possible.

Software manager Sarah in New Hampshire prefers an incremental approach to space progress. She believes when we return to the Moon, we should return to stay. Otherwise, she warns, what we accomplish will go to waste.

Engineer Vito in Colorado supports and incremental path forward to explore the Solar System. We currently have proven rockets, he points out. We have already landed humans to another planetary body. We have placed robotic spacecraft in orbit around Mars and landed rovers on its surface. We have been on a journey to Mars for 70 years. It's time to complete a new milestone, he insists.

My Preference

Personally, I no longer care how we do it. I no longer care who does it. I no longer care how long it takes or how large the budget needs to be or how efficient the mission architecture is. I want to see humanity expand outward in whatever way will get us there.

Supremacy of Sustainability

The reasons and details differ, but generally, millennials were of one mind: however we move forward, we need to do so to stay. For some millennials, that means an Apollo-like drive forward, and just as importantly, the funds to match. Without a budget increase, it's difficult to picture a large, unified effort to accomplish a grand mission as we did when we landed astronauts on the Moon for the first time 50 years ago.

For most millennials, financial, political, and technical realities have convinced them to prefer an incremental approach, a slow and steady drive forward toward our goals. However, a slower pace isn't without its shortcomings including changing political winds, program cancellations, cut funding, lost motivation, and lack of public interest. Despite these challenges, most millennials seem to agree an incremental approach is the best way forward to sustain the progress made.

CHAPTER 5
THE LONG VIEW

How Long is Too Long?

Fair or unfair, millennials have been nicknamed the Impatient Generation. Usually this label is in the context of career advancement and rewards. As a whole, millennials are considered ambitious and proactive, unwilling to wait long to get that promotion, earn that raise, become entrusted with leadership in that project, or gain those perks they were promised.

Various reasons are given for this seeming lack of patience in the career progression process. Employer/employee loyalty is not what is used to be. Long gone are the days when most employees can stay with an employer for decades and be rewarded for their time and labor. Millennials are much more aware they can be fired or laid off at any time for any reason with no remorse from their former employer. Why not get what they can from an employer while they are still employed? Why be patient in a system that does not reward patience? Millennials may also experience ageism, a bias against them because of their age, preventing them from obtaining promotions or leadership positions they may otherwise deserve.

Another potential reason for career impatience is financial necessity. With living costs increasing, student loan debt skyrocketing, and wages not keeping up, millennials need those higher-paying jobs, raises, promotions, and perks for their survival. When a raise means the difference between falling behind on bills or becoming financially stable, they will fight for the raise regardless of whether they seem impatient or overly ambitious.

As the saying goes, "Be the change you want to see in the world." Millennials, similar to perhaps all younger generations throughout history, have the energy and enthusiasm to put their ideas and ideals into action. When these efforts are slowed by bureaucracy, ageism, a lack of power or authority, or a status-quo mentality, millennials may express frustration. They see the need for change now, so why should they wait for the world to change to catch up with them?

Millennials may also be adjusting to the technology of the time. With easy, quick, always-accessible communications, modern society is becoming accustomed to rapid responses and fast changes. Yes, even from their coworkers and managers. Although older millennials may remember a time of dial-up internet and slow data transfer speeds, most millennials have grown up with increasingly near-instant connections. Click a link and it loads. Click a video and it plays. Mailing a paper letter rather than sending an email seems like a deliberate throwback to the slower-paced days of old. The world has changed. Naturally, the younger generations have changed with it.

I've probed this multifaceted concept by honing in on particular area of career-related patience: mission or project length. I asked our millennial panel whether mission length matters and how comfortable they are working on a mission that would continue on after they leave the workforce. How much does instant gratification factor into their work satisfaction? Do they need to witness the fruits of their labor to feel motivated?

Many panelists took the opportunity to discuss whether they believe mission length matters more generally, taking into account public opinion, funding, employee morale, scientific objectives, and other factors.

Shorter Views for Smaller Successes

Engineer Lindsay in Alabama would be hesitant to work on a program that wouldn't achieve its goals until after she's gone. She sees tremendous value in long-duration space missions such as NASA's *New Horizons* mission to Pluto and Kuiper belt object Arrokoth, launched in 2006. But she personally prefers her work with the ISS where she can experience nearly instant gratification knowing that her work enables scientists to do important space research now.

Astrophysicist Jacob in the United Kingdom prefers working on projects that would wrap up in a couple years so he can see it to completion. He wouldn't want to work on something that takes up the span of his entire career.

Student and museum tour guide Walter in Florida doesn't see himself working on a mission that will last past his lifetime. He would like to see his work come to fruition and become functional.

Aerospace engineer Eric in Alabama believes it's important that each participant in a major effort sees the fruits of their labor. Workers are able to develop ownership when they see their work bring about tangible accomplishments.

Human factors engineer Victor in Texas would prefer to see the fruition of his work in his lifetime. He wouldn't mind working on an ambitious long-term project so long as he was able to witness its completion. He approves of multi-generational missions with great scientific returns. But he believes the majority of our focus should be on the *now* to ensure we remain consistent in our efforts across generations.

Engineer Justin in Florida believes it's important for workers who start a program to be able to finish it. Multi-generational missions will have problems with workforce turnover and knowledge transfer, he warns.

Many great discoveries could span decades or lifetimes. Design engineer Rachel in Florida thinks that could be a problem. She argues that, psychologically, people need to see goals accomplished. She personally is willing to be patient to work on a mission that is worth waiting for, but she would still need to see progress. She needs that sense of accomplishment along the way and she knows she's not alone. She predicts a seemingly unending mission would drain enthusiasm and motivation.

Engineer Nathan in Colorado would be happy to work on a project that doesn't finish for a long time, even 500 years, so long as his work has an impact. But he worries very long-term missions wouldn't be supported by the public and would need to be broken up into smaller goals. It's difficult to get people invested in something they'll never see, he explains.

Engineer Nicholas in Texas keeps the human factor in mind. Keeping up the morale of his teams is of upmost importance to him. Accomplishing missions or mission objectives on a frequent basis does wonders to stimulate the morale of a team and improve job satisfaction to make any amount of work worth it, he explains. Amazing engineering feats and spectacular work successes inspire him to keep working even harder. But the longer the mission, the harder it becomes to keep up morale and keep track of ever-changing careers, reassignments, funding allotments, and other human factors. On the other hand, he admits large long-duration missions give us the sense of being part of something greater than ourselves.

The experience aerospace engineer Christopher in Colorado has working on CubeSats with short development cycles has given him an appreciation for quicker missions. Longer missions suffer from knowledge turnover and aging technology, he warns.

Safety engineer Kevin in Florida worries about staying motivated while working on a long-term mission. He believes it would be a continual challenge to ensure workers remember what they are working toward and see the big picture.

If a mission takes too long, it loses support and momentum, warns software manager Sarah in New Hampshire. She believes large missions should be broken down into smaller objectives to keep that momentum behind the project going. "I think that every mission is important and will help us learn about the universe around us, as well as things that will benefit life on earth and the survival of humanity."

Physicist Lindsey in Maryland prefers working on shorter missions or at least breaking longer missions into smaller milestones. Especially in government, it may be more difficult to attract personnel to longer-term missions because of the real risk of project cancellations and funding interruptions.

Mission length matters to engineer Alex in Georgia. He believes drawn-out budget disagreements squash public interest and potentially harm mission success. Costs only increase as we adapt older designs to new technology, he points out. And both lawmakers and taxpayers may change their minds over time, he adds.

Although aerospace engineer Darius in Alabama would personally work a mission that wouldn't be completed until after he retires, he worries about politics and public opinion. In his experience, missions that are too long cause the public to lose interest and question why the government is paying so much for the project. Because most of space exploration is still federally funded, he explains, public opinion sways elected officials who dictate direction and funding. Adequate progress must be made for a legitimate return on investment to taxpayers, he asserts.

Of course, a mission can take too long, astrobiologist Eddie in California insists. The longer the mission, he explains, the more difficult it becomes to maintain public interest and preserve adequate human and monetary capital to complete the current mission and pursue subsequent missions. But he believes that we, as an advanced technological species, should be taking the long view. He professes the importance of starting to tackle the generations-long projects now to cultivate the maturity that benefits the interplanetary society he hopes we one day become.

Eddie believes millennials are frustrated by the long

timescales of many space missions. He notes a pattern of spending years or even decades developing new technologies for a new space mission even when substantial science could be returned from redeploying existing technologies to new locations or applying these technologies to answer different questions. He believes mission planning and support is tilted toward new technology and facility development rather than scientific exploration. This is because of the process of how funding is allocated, at least in the United States. He believes there should be a better balance between short-term and long-term missions.

Geology graduate student Sean in Arizona believes that many long-duration missions shouldn't be rushed. But there's a risk in them dragging out too long, he warns. Longer missions may lose public interest and jeopardize their funding, for example. He predicts too long of a mission may even lose its focus and become inefficient and unfeasible. But he personally would have no problem working on a mission that completes after he's left the workforce. That's legacy, he declares.

Despite living in Australia, astronomer Brett in Queensland advocates for increasing NASA's budget. He hopes the American public will be excited by a grand vision for space exploration. He wants such a vision to include a sustained human presence on the Moon and Mars, and quickly. Missions that take too long risk losing public interest, effectively killing the mission, he explains. However, he warns, grand missions that are concluded by symbolically planting a "mission accomplished" flag do not lead to continued space exploration. He believes there must be a middle ground.

Astronomer Jen in Arkansas worries that the public will be less likely to support a long-duration mission that will not be realized in their lifetime. It will be harder for them to fathom the benefits of such a long mission, she explains. But she has no problems working on a long mission that would be completed after she left the workforce.

Astronomer Crystal in Maryland believes missions should be completed within a person's lifetime. If a generation does not see progress made on an investment, later generations may be less likely to go big, she concludes.

Biomedical engineer Jordan in British Columbia worries about the physical and psychological limitations of sending an astronaut on a long-term mission to Mars. He also wonders about the physical limitations of the spacecraft and its technology. He foresees most long-term missions will be incremental in nature and build on the successes of prior missions.

The fragility of the human body is a limiter to long-term human spaceflight explains biology student Skye in Florida. She wonders if the risks are too great for long-term space habitation. The effects of space radiation and the lack of Earth's gravity on human physiology have been well studied and the results are troubling, she exclaims. Astronauts have experienced short- and long-term complications with bone and muscle atrophy, cardiovascular system functions, red blood cell production, balance, eyesight, immune system functions, and more.

Regardless of the challenges, Skye is personally willing to put her life and health on the line for the progress of human spaceflight. "They can pay me a billion dollars to be an astronaut or they can pay me absolutely nothing and I will be happy either way because I am doing what I love," she declares.

The Long View

Engineer Vito in Colorado would work on a long-duration mission, but only if the main mission was broken up into sub-missions. He worries that funding, morale, and politics wouldn't support a long-term mission without interim accomplishments, but to him, it's worth it. He points to the longevity of *Voyager* (two deep space probes launched in 1977 that are still operational), *Mars Odyssey* (launched in 2001 and is still operational), and *Mars Exploration Rover Opportunity* (launched in 2003, lost contact in 2018). All of these were long-term planetary exploration missions that needed few resources to continue transmitting valuable data.

NASA is a critical catalyst in the private space ecosystem, computer scientist Michael explains. NASA's co-dependence with shifting political administrations is culpable for ruining many long-term missions. Yet despite this political uncertainty, he is impressed that NASA has managed to accomplish missions. He sees NASA's approach working best with longer-term goals such as settling space. On the other hand, private space companies need shorter timelines, he explains. He believes dynamic companies can push NASA to be more efficient with their mission timelines.

Computer engineer Joslyn in Florida doesn't mind longer missions so long as there are many smaller phases and milestones along the way. Longer missions have the benefit of job stability and a greater sense of accomplishment. She points to the *Voyager* probes which are still providing unparalleled information about our Solar System and beyond.

Engineer Lyndsay in Virginia supports long-duration missions so long as the work produces value along the way. She would happily serve on a mission that extended past her time in the workforce so long as it provided value for the time and cost.

Long-term missions for scientific benefit are most important to science reporter Leah in Massachusetts. Thoroughly planned longer missions come with a greater depth and breadth of study, which are important to furthering our scientific understanding. Government funding instability can disrupt longer missions and interfere with the scientific process, but that wouldn't stop her from working on a long-term scientific project.

Astrobiologist Marie in California thinks long-term. Many of the Solar System science missions she works on or hopes to work on will outlast her career. These programs can last decades from mission idea to funded proposal to spacecraft launch to mission operations and even through extended mission operations, she explains. Some millennials find themselves working on space programs that were created before they were born, she points out.

In some cases, Marie continues, mission principal investigators and project scientists have succession plans. It's not realistic that one person would be able to see a large program or deep space mission through, she explains. She assures us most space scientists understand they may only work on a specific mission for a few years and then move on to the next mission. She and her colleagues have worked on several missions and expect to continue to work on new ones.

Smaller missions are less constrained by mission length, engineer Paige in California points out. She praises the *New Horizons* mission. Launched in 2006, the public essentially forgot about the deep space probe for nine years. However, in July 2015, the world was united in the excitement of the spacecraft flying by Pluto and catching a new glimpse of this distant world.

As a scientist, graduate student Gabe in Arizona supports missions with maximum scientific value regardless of mission length. He cites *New Horizons* as a mission with a long timeline that is inspiring younger generations. *New Horizons* increased our knowledge of icy bodies in the outer Solar System, he explains. These data help us understand the history and distribution of water in our Solar System, he adds. He believes *New Horizons*' discoveries also serve as an invaluable educational outreach tool for the next-generation workforce.

When humans aren't at risk, which is the case with robotic missions exploring deep space, the length of the mission is of no concern to planetary scientist Ryan in Missouri. She believes scientific results from long-term missions such as *New Horizons* were well worth the wait. She would be pleased to work on a mission that wouldn't be completed until after her time. For her, there is satisfaction that comes from being involved in something she knows will return great science, even if she doesn't get to see those results. "I would love to lay the steppingstone for the next generation."

Planetary scientist Kelsi in Colorado acknowledges her debt of gratitude to the colleagues who came before her who worked for decades to propose, design, build, and launch the planetary science missions she works on today. Some of her older colleagues retired before their missions made it to their destinations. Yet that's okay, longer missions are fine with her. There are some science objectives that would not ever be realized if we only stuck with shorter missions, she explains.

The specifics of space projects are less important to businesswoman Carolyn in Colorado. Destination, mission length, motivations – those are all details to her. She would personally find it compelling to work on a mission that extended for generations, providing unique data and lessons learned.

Money is no object for businessman Barry in Florida and neither is time. It doesn't matter to him how long a space mission takes so long as the results are interesting.

He foresees single missions someday spanning whole careers of astronauts. In fact, he believes humanity is destined to someday leave planet Earth to explore the stars. "God be with those brave souls who choose to go."

Mechanical engineer Tracie in Alabama is gratified to be able to contribute to something far greater than herself. Resources are finite, she explains. She believes we will eventually need to leave this planet to sustain our species. Living off-world is an incredibly hard thing to do which is why we need to start now, she insists. The work she and her colleagues do is truly about leaving a mark on the future and enabling humanity to become a multi-planet species. She quotes Warren Buffett: "Someone's sitting in the shade today because someone planted a tree a long time ago."[17] She realizes she may never sit in the shade of the tree she's helping to plant, but she's okay with that. Her work is about building a better future. "I may not get to retire on Mars or ever go to space myself, but someone will in part because of the work we're doing every day."

Aerospace engineer Mason in Alabama likes the idea of working on a mission that will continue on after he is no longer working on it. He appreciates the legacy he would leave working on a long project. It would be like planting seeds that would then grow, mature, and take on new forms, he explains. He would not see the payoff himself, but he would know that someone else will sit and enjoy the

---

17 Kilpatrick, Andrew. *Of Permanent Value: The Story of Warren Buffett*. Andy Kilpatrick Publishing Empire, 2006.

shade of the tree he planted.

Aerospace engineer Logan in Alabama supports long-term Mars exploration and settlement which motivate his own work drive. He doesn't believe there is such a thing as a mission extending too far into the future. He would absolutely work on a mission that completed after he left. Hopefully a human Mars program outlast him, he imagines.

Mechanical engineer Chelsea in Florida dreams of the day when humans will live beyond LEO permanently. Her dream may take longer than her lifetime to accomplish and that's fine by her. While she's still around, she's doing her part by working on NASA's Orion capsule. She believes someday Orion may take humankind to the Moon, Mars, and deep space.

The timescale needed for a grand mission doesn't bother astrobiologist Joshua in California. He isn't deterred by a far-off future payoff. He's looking forward to the 2030s when new space telescopes begin operations to systematically search for life on exoplanets. He will be midway through his career by then. He doesn't have a problem working on a mission that won't be completed until after he is retired or dead. We strive to build a better future we probably won't live to see, he explains, in space and in other aspects of our lives.

Engineer and businessman Dan in Pennsylvania doesn't mind working on a mission that takes years to complete. He points to historical grand human achievements in the great cathedrals of Europe and the great pyramids of Egypt, which took years to complete. To him, spaceflight is no different.

Astrophysics student Xzavier in Florida would love to see missions he works on completed during his lifetime but he understands this isn't always possible. He doesn't believe a mission can extend too far into the future as long as the resources are available to support it. Whether he's there to see the end of a mission or not, he hopes it benefits the next generation.

To aerospace engineer Yasmin in Florida, mission length matters less than mission quality. She would not hesitate to join a mission she wholeheartedly believed in even if it was to be completed beyond her lifetime.

Aerospace engineering student Richard in Washington does not care if the mission he is working on is completed after he leaves the workforce. What matters more to him is the purpose of the mission and whether he is able to pay the bills.

Geomorphology graduate student Stephanie in California would work on a mission that might not be enacted until after she was out of the workforce. She sees such a mission as a way of giving a boost to the next generation. She doesn't believe mission length matters as much as the end goal.

Engineer and data scientist Nikolai in the Czech Republic understands the long-term mindset needed for such grand space visions. Surely we are all in this together, he states, generation after generation. He views his ideas as being like children, nurturing them for a time and letting them grow into their own. "I would always be willing to let someone else inherit my work, and would graciously do so, so that it could live on beyond my own influence."

Space policy professional Nate in Washington, DC is inspired by NASA's *Voyager* probes, launched before millennials were born, still exploring the depths of interstellar space today, continuing to produce data after decades. He thinks it would be a powerful legacy to work on long-term grand missions that continued on after he retires.

Engineer Mark in Virginia does not believe a mission or project can last too long. He would happily work on a project that he would never see completed. Space exploration is not about the individual, he explains. It's about all of us. Pushing the frontier enriches us both spiritually and materially, he reflects.

My View

I see the benefits of both short-term and long-term thinking. Each project I work on is short-term, sometimes very short term by design. Yet as a whole, in a tiny way, I hope to contribute to the progress of humanity in space and the scientific questions of our time. Everything I do short term, I hope in some small way contributes to humanity long-term. For so many of the reasons above, I believe we should embrace a combination of short- and long-term goals in a diverse portfolio of space missions. There's no reason why we can't enjoy the fruits of our labor today and work toward a better tomorrow.

Impatient with Progress, Patient with Goals

Millennials are mixed on their opinions on project mission length. Some millennials have concerns about workforce morale, public support, long-term funding, and the challenges of long-distance space travel. Some millennials preferr to reap the rewards of their labor and see their work to completion. Some millennials are personally willing to work on a long-term project but still have reservations about a long-term approach.

Many millennials see value in longer-term thinking, especially for scientific missions. Some millennials would feel honored to work on a project lasting longer than their lifetime, benefiting future generations and leaving a legacy. Many millennials advocate for breaking grand missions into smaller goals to celebrate the smaller successes while keeping an eye on the prize.

CHAPTER 6
HOW PERILOUS THE PATH

Risky Behavior

In the human spaceflight world, there's a balance to be had between staying reasonably safe and taking risks. There are no hard rules about what's reasonable, just hard discussions.

Another label millennials seem to be stuck with is risk-averse. This is usually claimed in the context of avoiding financial risks, saving more than they're spending, and making conservative investments. This is an unsurprising trait given the financial instability and economic turmoil millennials have grown up in. During the financial crisis of 2007 and 2008, many older millennials were unemployed or underemployed with high levels of student loan debt. Some millennials take great care not to take risks that endanger their livelihoods or financial stability.

Others believe millennials may have been raised to be less open to taking risks based on how they were parented, for better or for worse. Over the past few decades, parenting in Western society has become more hands-on and safety-focused. Parental attitudes have shifted toward more supervised play and organized activities rather than "free range" and unstructured play. Many millennials were warned of "stranger danger" as children. Products and environments have become more safety-focused to minimize child injury, death, or harm. Few would argue that's not a positive trend. However, some believe the lack of freedom to take risks in childhood creates more risk-averse adults.

Especially older millennials, but likely all millennials in the United States were strongly influenced by the September 11, 2001 attacks and the resulting conflicts. Many older millennials remember that defining moment in their childhoods or earlier adulthoods and can recount exactly where they were when they saw or heard of the fall of the Twin Towers in New York City. The following years brought the seemingly never-ending War Against Terror. It's difficult to determine how these events have shaped millennials' risk tolerance regarding war, national security, and personal security.

Paradoxically, millennials are undeniably more open to taking risks with online security. Having grown up in the internet age, providing information online is second nature to most millennials. Many millennials do not expect to lead perfectly private lives online. Millennials may be aware that social media platforms and consumer companies are collecting and selling their information, but most millennials appear unconcerned. Additionally, most millennials trust their truly sensitive information is being properly guarded by companies entrusted with it such as financial institutions, insurance companies, and government agencies. Millennials are much more open to using online conveniences such as e-banking and e-commerce than older generations, trusting their sensitive information will be kept secure.

Millennials aren't the only ones labeled risk-averse, fairly or unfairly. Current-day NASA leadership has also been accused of not taking the risks it once did, for better or for worse. Those who make this criticism believe NASA's risk aversion is holding the agency back from advancing its grander goals. Many who see NASA as less risk-tolerant also see emerging space companies as more risk-tolerant, taking big risks for potential big payoffs.

After the devastating astronaut crew losses of Space Shuttles *Challenger* (1986) and *Columbia* (2003), many believe NASA's focus on a safety culture is a positive evolution. *Challenger* broke up upon launch, losing its crew of seven astronauts. *Columbia* broke up as it returned home, losing its crew of seven. Investigations into both incidents determined that a loose safety culture contributed to the disasters.

I asked our millennial panel how comfortable they felt taking risk and how important safety was to them in space missions. Most were on the same page: safety is a top priority, but eliminating all risk is impossible. Some internalized the question. Some considered the question of risk in the abstract. And some brought to mind the astronauts they work with, real people who risk their lives for their missions.

Better To Be Safe Than Sorry

As a safety engineer, safety is the top priority for Rachel in Florida. Every mission has some risk involved, she admits. She believes training and redundancies can reduce risk. "We can replace technology, but any human lost is one too many, and irreplaceable."

Space is one of the few industries where safety is a concern above profit, aerospace engineer Anthony in California explains. A great deal of time and effort is dedicated to ensuring that systems work correctly, he adds. To him, safety is a top priority to ensure mission success. Mission failure at any point wastes a lot of money, he points out, so governments and companies make sure the mission will perform correctly and safely before launch.

Safety is absolutely the number-one priority for aerospace engineer Darius in Alabama. So much of his work, including meetings, paperwork, and panels, contribute to a safety culture by seeking out every minor mistake. His workplace showcases pictures of the ill-fated crews of *Apollo 1* (whose crew of three was lost in a ground fire), the Space Shuttle *Challenger*, and the Space Shuttle *Columbia* to remind him and his coworkers of what can happen if they get complacent. It serves as a daily reminder for him that safety must be a top priority. Human spaceflight will always be inherently risky, he adds, and astronauts accept that risk.

Engineer Tom in Florida focuses on his project's immediate goals: the upgrades, the tests, the upcoming flights of new hardware, and all the steps in between. Safety is a high priority for him. Workplace culture has ingrained the importance of safety in everything he touches, whether humans will be on the rocket or not.

Human factors engineer Victor in Texas admits there are many things that can go wrong in space. He knows risk will always be part of the mission in some form or fashion. But he believes if a human is involved, safety and well-being should always be the top priority. He challenges management at every level of an organization to be the responsible parties for upholding this top priority.

Safety should be a top priority, but software manager Sarah in New Hampshire doesn't believe that's the current reality. It seems to her that money and public perception are the current top priorities. But high-profile launch accidents harm public opinion and lessen public support for space activities, she warns. Additionally, long delays in space progress also harm public opinion and waste money. Businesses and government agencies alike do what they can do look good and either make or save money, she criticizes. Yet she thinks emphasis on safety should override those concerns. We should be modeling proper behavior now for the space industry of the future, she asserts.

Safety is always the top priority for aerospace engineer Kelly in Florida. Safety should never be compromised for schedule or funding, she states. She knows that if a rocket design is rushed because of a demanding deadline, astronaut lives could be at stake. Human life is more valuable than any price tag, she counsels.

Safety is also the number one priority for aerospace engineer Eric in Alabama. He insists the loss of life is unacceptable with the tools, experience, and risk mitigation methods the space industry has used for decades. Under no circumstances does he believe it should be acceptable to risk loss of life for cost, schedule, or internal trade secrets. No corners should be cut, he warns.

In addition to patience and progress, design engineer Rachel in Florida values safety. The inherent risk in space exploration is part of the excitement and the adrenaline rush, but her respect for human life encourages her to take the utmost care in making sure everyone returns home safely, "to their family or their 15 cats." She insists we should never put money first over people or cut corners to get things done more quickly because we are impatient.

No Risk No Reward

Science educator John in Florida envisions himself as a future flight surgeon and astronaut. His enthusiasm for human space travel is balanced with his understanding of aircraft flight safety. "Going to a flight school, the first thing you learn is that safety is always the top priority in the aircraft." Regardless of the mission or destination, safety is always the top priority for him. But if given the choice to fly to space, he would "boldly go," acknowledging that, to him, it's worth the risk.

Geology graduate student Sean in Arizona believes safety is a top priority, especially when it comes to crewed missions. "To put it bluntly, you don't have a human-led mission or science if you lose your crew." Skimping on safety is not only dangerous for the astronauts, he warns, it also jeopardizes the future of subsequent human exploration missions.

Engineer and CEO Mark in Kentucky insists we need to accept a higher risk tolerance to advance space systems and vehicles. We need to characterize the performance of these systems. But once humans are involved, he believes safety must be the priority. He doesn't see these as opposing mindsets.

Working directly with astronauts reminds engineer Genevieve in Texas they are people like you and me. They have families who love them and they are not willing to take unnecessary risks with their lives. "Every day I discuss those risks, and I look over at my friends, and have a gut check if I feel like the risk is acceptable for them or not."

Nothing is guaranteed, not even safety, despite the cultural emphasis on putting safety first, explains mechanical engineer Chelsea in Florida. She knows putting astronauts inside the hardware she helps create and launching them into the hostile environment of space is inherently dangerous. We cannot control every aspect of a mission, she admits, especially a novel one. We strive to make a mission as safe as possible, but she believes we must be willing to accept some risks. "If we wanted to keep astronauts completely safe, without risk, on a Mars mission, robots would be the planet's only visitors." That doesn't sit right with her. She doesn't dream of robots settling the Solar System.

Working closely with ISS astronauts has given aerospace engineer April in Texas a new perspective on safety and risk. Engineers do their best to mitigate risks, but there just aren't many ways to make a controlled explosion safe, she explains. The astronauts she works with absolutely understand the risks. The way she sees it, many astronauts seek out risky positions as part of their nature.

Engineer Nicholas in Texas puts himself in the shoes of any astronaut relying on his space hardware. Would he himself feel safe flying on this mission? Would he let one of his family members fly in this hardware? How confident is he in his own design, the work of his hands? He isn't satisfied until he is confident in his work to the point where he would let a family member fly on his hardware on a hypothetical mission to space.

Astrophysics student Xzavier in Florida is personally not comfortable becoming an astronaut himself. So he doesn't feel comfortable dictating the amount of risk someone else is willing to take travel to space. He supports those individuals brave enough to step up and take on this tremendous task to progress space exploration.

Regarding human spaceflight, businesswoman Carolyn in Colorado summed up her thoughts by quoting pioneering astronaut Virgil "Gus" Grissom, "The conquest of space is worth the risk of life."[18]

Astronauts understand the risks when they get in a spacecraft, engineer Nathan in Colorado explains, just as car drivers and passengers understand the risks of car accidents. Space travel, just like anything else, will never achieve 0% risk of serious injury or death. Risk must be accepted as a reality, though it should be minimized, he adds.

Biomedical engineer Jordan in British Columbia fully accepts the risks of spaceflight. He recognizes the benefits outweigh the risks. Safety is a top priority but it is balanced with a calculated risk assessment, he adds. He points to the Apollo missions as inherently dangerous. But those working on the Apollo missions made them as reliable and safe as possible within the time and budget constraints. He believes Apollo produced significant scientific advancements which outweighed the risks.

---

18 Grissom, Virgil. *Gemini: A Personal Account of Man's Venture Into Space*. MacMillan Publishing Company, 1968.

Biology student Skye in Florida sees a future where human spaceflight will become as common as commercial air transportation. However, before we get to that step, she believes we have a lot of testing to do. Better be safe than sorry, she recommends. But she points out astronauts sign on to take the risks. In her opinion, risk is acceptable when stepping out into the unknown and exploring foreign worlds. She longs to take that step herself.

Planetary scientist Ryan in Missouri believes we humans have an innate desire to explore and should not be limited to exploring Earth. There are many things humans can do more effectively than robots can, so we must continue sending humans to space, she insists. Without risk-taking, she believes we will limit new discoveries, scientific advancement, and an extended human presence in space. She expects we will never accomplish grand goals without accepting some degree of risk.

However, Ryan is concerned about the risks to humans due to long-term spaceflight such as radiation exposure, psychological issues, and other risk factors. This may limit the time and therefore the distance humans can travel in space unless these risks can be adequately addressed. But all humans have free will, she reminds us. She believes as long as it's not forced, astronauts should have the personal choice to take risks they are comfortable with.

Engineer Tom in Florida also envisions a future in which humans live on other planets such as Mars. Although safety is and will always be a top priority for him, he acknowledges the inherent risk of space travel could be acceptable for future travelers breaking ground on new martian habitats. He believes even one-way trips in which martian settlers are willing and expected to die off-Earth might be worth it for the potential gain. He's so confident in this dream that he believes millennials will be the first to put footprints on Mars, inspiring the following generations to expand even more out into the cosmos. But he won't be volunteering anytime soon.

The dangers of space travel are worth it to engineer and space policy professional Jane in Texas. Those who willingly take on the risks understand them, she explains. However, for space travel to be available to a larger percentage of the human population, she insists that safety needs to be at the forefront of all aspects of design and operations. "If the initial travelers, as risk tolerant as they may be, are injured or worse, it will make it significantly more difficult for the industry to flourish and for the average citizen to be willing to spend their money on such endeavors."

Aerospace engineer Logan in Alabama holds up failure as one of the best learning tools. Yet he worries about failures involving human lives, especially in private human spaceflight. He fears public outcry over human losses could halt the young industry for years. As the industry matures, he hopes spaceflight will become more routine and failures won't stop operations, just as car accidents don't stop the automotive industry.

Engineer and businessman Dan in Pennsylvania sees risk as something to mitigate but not be eliminated. Risk can't be eliminated, he insists. If we are to undertake space activities, we have to accept that risk is inherent to pushing forward the state of the art, he asserts. "Certainly Orville and Wilbur Wright's first flights were very risky, but I think we're all glad they decided to push ahead anyway," he says. The Wright brothers designed, built, and flew the first successful airplane in 1903, a dangerous undertaking at the time.

Engineer Kyle in Washington likens the spaceflight industry to the early aviation industry. He points to society's willingness to accept early accidents in aviation which led to lessons learned. "The industry was given permission to fail, and fail they did. But through these failures came a series of solutions that now enable us to call air travel one of the safer forms of transportation." He believes the space industry will need to learn these same hard lessons to grow human spaceflight. But we can approach it differently now by analyzing existing data and simulating scenarios, he explains. He knows we will still make mistakes, but we will learn from them.

At this point in our technological development, aerospace engineer Yasmin in Florida does not believe there should be many casualties in spaceflight. We have better tools now compared to the early days of the space age, she explains. She understands risk is always a factor when doing something new that has never before been tried. Only then is relatively high risk acceptable to her.

Computer engineer Joslyn in Florida upholds the principle of preparing for the worst scenario but not fearing the uncertain. Safety is a top priority for her, but she accepts risk. She believes we should learn from the mistakes of the past and incorporate those lessons learned into current and future missions. Risk is inevitable and necessary for missions to unexplored places using unproven technology, she asserts.

Aerospace engineer Floyd in Iowa accepts that there's a certain amount of risk inherent to space missions. He files the proper paperwork, does what he can to mitigates against damage, and prioritizes safety, but not above everything else. "Hope for the best, prepare for the worst," is his motto.

Engineer Mark in Virginia is comfortable accepting risk in space along with the consequences of that risk. However, he warns, safety and protocol are important. He believes taking great risks with equally great payoffs should be the norm so long as we mitigate against danger as much as possible.

Engineer and world traveler JP accepts some risk in space missions. There will always be risk, he insists. He believes the goal should be to minimize the risk to some acceptable level. "I find it unfortunate that we can accept these losses when it's for war but not when it's for science."

Engineer Lindsay in Alabama concludes that, "the only way to eliminate all risk in space missions is to stop doing them. I don't think that is the right answer." Everyone involved in designing and operating space missions needs to understand the consequences of failure and buy down risk as much as possible, she advises.

Mechanical engineer Tracie in Alabama knows risk is inherent in human spaceflight. There's no such thing as a routine launch, she explains. Redundancies are built into the system to mitigate risk. We all conduct risk assessments daily, she adds, whether getting into a car, irradiating oneself with a medical scan, or designing a space mission. "We as engineers are always trying to do absolutely everything we can to reduce the risk of catastrophic failures, but that probability will always be nonzero." She counsels that we have to live with that uncertainty.

Student and museum tour guide Walter in Florida is passionate about reducing yet accepting risk. "But, if you concern yourself with reducing every single possible risk you'll never leave the ground in the first place." He emphasizes: we may as well stay home if we are not comfortable with the idea that there is risk involved in spaceflight. He objects to using the word "safety" when referring to, "lighting a 200 foot tall telephone pole full of explosives on fire, hurling it out of the atmosphere, flying through the space environment itself, then basically riding a meteor during atmospheric reentry." He doesn't believe what he calls an "everyday safety" metric is the best way to think about spaceflight. Risk reduction is better, he insists, and spaceflight is still experimental.

Corporate communicator Evan in Washington, DC believes risk is unavoidable and therefore acceptable. If there are no risks, he says, it's probably a sign we are not doing anything worthwhile. He believes risk is part of exploration and discovery. Safety is a top priority and we should do everything we can to mitigate risk, but he counsels that risk will always exist.

Engineer Vito in Colorado believes in managing risk depending on the value of the risked asset. He worries less about the loss of an inexpensive CubeSat than the loss of expensive planetary science hardware or an astronaut.

As a scientist, astrophysicist Jacob in the United Kingdom believes there's a balance to be had between taking risks and gaining scientific returns. In space exploration, he believes the scientific returns outweigh the risks. He knows the returns can be great: national pride, technological progress, and exploring the unknown. Yet he doesn't believe the science is worth it if it human harm is essentially guaranteed.

In addition to human loss, geology graduate student Gabe in Arizona highlights the potential loss of significant financial space investments including astronaut training, vehicle development, and launch cost. He warns taxpayers are at risk of losing their investment and subsequently their trust in legislators and space exploration in general following an accident. He believes taxpayer scrutiny helps shape priorities for safety, budget, and mission timeline.

Computer scientist Michael believes the best approach to space exploration is to build autonomously in space before humans ever arrive. This strategy may increase safety for human missions, he explains. He knows there will never be 0% risk. He believes we must accept a little risk.

Engineer Justin in Florida believes that while safety is

always the top priority, risk is acceptable in certain situations. Without a certain level of accepted risk, he worries we wouldn't ever do anything new. Not only is risk acceptable in his mind, it is necessary.

Engineer Nicholas in Washington believes it's human nature to progress, to grow, to improve, and to spread around the globe and around the galaxy. But he admits it's not without risk. It's no surprise that such a dreamer would accept the risk for the sake of the dream, he adds. So long as the risk-takers are aware of the dangers and take reasonable precautions, he believes the risk is worth the potential payoff.

Business consultant Liam in Virginia believes greatness is born from the risks we take. He believes safety should be a vital part of any major human spaceflight project. Yet if we excessively focus on the risk, he fears we will hold ourselves back from progress and from the greatness we desire. He desires another era of rapid space technological advancement as was seen in the generations before at the dawn of the space age.

I, too, accept the risk of progressing forward into the unknown. I would personally take that risk: to put my life on the line, to potentially die to be part of something greater than myself, but never recklessly. I trust the professionals in the space sector to do their jobs to ensure cargo and crew are as safe as they reasonably can be. Yet I also acknowledge there's a point of diminishing returns. I'm ready to take risks to move humanity outward. Are you?

Assessing and Accepting Risk

Most millennials are on the same page: spaceflight will never be completely safe but we should take care not to take unnecessary risks, especially when lives are at stake. Some millennials have more of an emphasis on the level of safety needed and the use of tools to learn from previous mistakes and mitigate against risk. Others lean in the other direction, feeling too much of an emphasis on safety inhibits progress. While some millennials place a higher priority on safety, few would define themselves as risk-averse.

CHAPTER 7
MULTITASKERS EXTRAORDINAIRE

How Much do Millennials Multitask?

Technology has the ability to change our methods, habits, and even our brains. Computers and mobile smart devices have accelerated this change. The transition from computers with a single display and a single command line to windowed computers allowed users to work on multiple tasks simultaneously. This ability increased as technology got more capable and accessible. Now, it's the norm to see a user's attention split between a smartphone in hand and another task, conversation, or entertainment device, both existing seamlessly, with perhaps additional lower-priority undertakings happening in the background.

Multitasking is executing more than one program or task at a time. This term originated in the computer industry and broadened to include the way people operate. Millennials grew up in a world that rapidly rapid embraced multitasking-enabling technology. It's the world millennial consumers helped form. Multitasking with technology is ingrained into the millennial lifestyle.

Technology is lauded for its ability to make us more efficient and productive. For many, multitasking is a way to stay connected to friends and the outside world. For others, multitasking is a way to challenge their minds and learn new skills. And yet for others, multitasking is an unpleasant necessity in a society that demands ever more productivity. For better or for worse, multitasking-enabling technology has changed how most of us operate.

Yet multitasking doesn't come without its pitfalls. Our accessible technology can distract us, divide our attention, limit our environmental awareness, and even harm our job performance. And yet some studies show that millennials and generation Z have adapted so fully to electronic distractions that their job performance can be enhanced by multitasking. However, there's no denying that multitasking shortens attention spans. It can also shift our mindsets from longer-term deeper thinking to shorter-term shallow task management. Notifications such as new emails, comments, and text messages activate the reward signals in our brain, becoming more of an addition than a conscious choice to multitask.

Multitasking may be second nature for millennials, but do they prefer it? Or would they rather not? To find out, I asked our millennial panel how they feel about multitasking, especially in the workplace. The preferences were decidedly mixed. Many millennials appreciate the benefits, but some feel they operate best when they don't. Millennials may be well adapted to multitasking, but not all of them like it.

Always Juggling

Aerospace engineer Kelly in Florida prefers to multitask. She finds working on one project at a time to be monotonous. She likes to be challenged by switching her mindset to solve different problems throughout the day.

Aerospace engineer Brad is a multitasker. Working two or three projects at a time allows him to stay alert and excited about his work. He feels multitasking keeps him from becoming too stagnant.

Mechanical engineer Chelsea in Florida has a job that allows her to work on multiple pieces of the same mission. She enjoys the freedom to multitask and manage different priorities. Someday she thinks it would be quite fun to work on multiple missions simultaneously. She enjoys the intellectual challenge of the balance.

Space communicator Calvin in New Mexico works best when he can choose between multiple projects with the flexibility to prioritize one project over another.

Biomedical engineer Jordan in British Columbia prefers to work on one main mission while working a couple small projects in parallel. Focusing on one primary project allows him to stay focused and drive progress further. The diversity of projects help to refresh his mind and think of new ways to approach and solve problems.

Businesswoman Crystal in Texas prefers working on multiple projects at a time to keep her mind stimulated with new things that spark her creativity and inspiration. When she hits a roadblock, she focuses on something else for a while. When she has a thought about a project she's not currently working on, she jots it down in a notebook to come back to later.

Studying, space educational outreach volunteering, and keeping up with her activity on social media are second nature to biology student Skye in Florida. "I find [multitasking] oddly relaxing." The challenge of multitasking ensures that she never gets bored. She paraphrases the common expression, "Ask a busy person to do something and it will get done."

Multitasking is vital for engineer and data scientist Nikolai in the Czech Republic when work moves too slowly to maintain his motivation. He works on multiple projects to combat stagnation and to keep moving himself forward. Yet he has so many ideas and projects on his plate, he sometimes feels overwhelmed. It helps him to switch topics entirely, working on a project in one field while researching work in an entirely different field to keep his mind fresh.

Nikolai can get so caught up in his work that he forgets the basic bodily necessities and forgoes meals and sleep. To combat this tendency, he tries to be more mindful of his daily routine and sets limits on his daily work hours.

Engineer Nicholas in Texas likes to work on a mix of one overarching mission with multiple smaller missions. In his mind, the smaller missions can be completed more quickly and provide tangible job satisfaction while the large, overarching mission gives a sense of purpose and an "all hands on deck" feel.

Aerospace engineer Mason in Alabama prefers to work on a variety of projects within the same mission. Working similar projects under the same umbrella allows him to better understand the relationships and interactions between projects. Working multiple projects at once keeps things interesting for him and keeps his mind and skills sharp. Yet he worries that if he worked on multiple missions at once, he might confuse different mission architectures and systems.

Astrobiologist Marie in California prefers to multitask with multiple projects in different phases. These new challenges within the project cycles keep the work exciting, even when focusing on the long-term. Projects in early phases open up a world of possibilities, including the human element of building a team from scratch. Newly operational missions produce exciting new data never before seen. Older missions have the tantalizing challenge of demanding creativity with routine data and well-used older scientific instruments to find new discoveries, she continues. She feels that each phase in a mission's lifetime has its own stresses and rewards.

Astronomer Rodrigo in New York multitasks a lot. "Not all research projects pan out, and many end up (unexpectedly) being a lot more rewarding than others; it's good not to put all your eggs in one basket."

Aerospace engineer Darius in Alabama prefers to work on multiple projects so as not to feel his work is getting stale doing the same thing over and over. Boredom breeds complacency, "which is very very bad in this type of work." Working multiple projects at once allows him to view things from different perspectives and helps to keep his mind sharp. It also prevents him from getting shoehorned into becoming the "go-to" person on a particular expertise. The existence of a "go-to" specialist can slow a project down if that expert becomes unavailable, he cautions.

Working on just one thing at a time can get boring for space policy professional Nate in Washington, DC. Unless it's a critical issue, he prefers to multitask, as long as the task juggling doesn't get too overwhelming, that is. He prefers working on multiple projects that are complementary or related, gaining on-the-job training through experience.

Geodesist Ryan in Colorado prefers multitasking within

reason. Too much commitment to a single project can become boring for him. His output can suffer if he's not properly stimulated by new and interesting tasks. Having one large project with occasional side investigations to learn new techniques or resolve anomalous results keeps him on his toes without diminishing his sense of purpose.

Geology graduate student Gabe in Arizona works on multiple projects simultaneously which allows him to stay up-to-date on a variety of scientific techniques. This diversity of missions helps him understand the differences between geologists, physicists, and chemists. He appreciates the challenge of reaching across disciplines and having fruitful collaborations.

Engineering student Amoree in Georgia is soaking up skills while in school: astronomy, CubeSat building, in-space communications, coding, circuitry, design, and many others. With this diversity of skills, she is preparing herself for a career in the space industry. Working on multiple projects at once allows her to maximize her experiences and explore her career options within the space sector.

Planetary scientist Kelsi in Colorado prefers to focus on what she is doing in the moment. However, that doesn't mean she doesn't work on different projects throughout the day. As a planetary scientist, it is rare for her to ever just be working on one project. She must keep expanding her knowledge and skills to produce new science. Working on multiple projects is critical for her to keep an eye out for future projects that could be proposed for grant funding.

One thing mechanical engineer Tracie in Alabama loves about working at NASA is the opportunity to work on multiple projects simultaneously. When she worked in the private sector, she sometimes felt that the job she started with was the same job she would still be doing when she retired. "For me, NASA always feels like a floor rather than a ceiling – the opportunities are boundless if you are willing to work hard and commit yourself to the mission."

Astrobiologist Eddie in California is used to taking the long view. Similar to Marie, Eddie is a scientist who participates in scientific missions at various stages of maturity. He juggles multiple projects at a time which he believes is beneficial. He explains that experience in one area can almost instantaneously inform another area.

Satellite engineer Adam in Colorado prefers to work on several projects at once. Processes and solutions discovered working on one project can benefit similar projects. When a temporary roadblock forces him to take a break from one project, he switches to another to work on in the meantime. He finds it rewarding to complete a short-term project. But what really fulfills him is working on a mission that extends far into the future and is part of a larger goal.

Bioengineer Diana in California find she is most productive with one long-term main project and a few short-term smaller side projects. Whenever she feels blocked working on the main project, she can switch to a side project. Progress on smaller projects allows her to feel more engaged in her work.

Geographer Chloe in the United Kingdom feels she learns more from working multiple projects simultaneously. She believes there is an opportunity for crucial feedback loops of knowledge and side-by-side learning with multi-tasking.

Even natural multitaskers have difficulty juggling too many projects. Scientist Anne in Washington enjoys working on two or three projects at a time. However, due to the nature of her work, she often has significantly more items on her to-do list than she would like.

Recent cutbacks and layoffs have given engineer Tom in Florida additional responsibilities that require him to multitask. These delays and setbacks frustrate him. He feels limited by the authorities above him. If only they would fund the program sustainably, he and his coworkers could do so much more. Seeing his work literally soar to the skies makes it all worth it, however.

Single-Task Focused

Engineer Hayley in California easily works on multiple projects at one time. However, she sees an advantage to focusing on one project or two interrelated projects at a time. She worries about being spread too thin otherwise.

Science reporter Leah in Massachusetts recognizes that multitasking is a required skill in today's world. But she likes to focus her attention and energy on one primary project at a time. Non-critical non-urgent side projects that don't detract from her primary project fit into her work style well.

Ideally, computer scientist Michael would work on one main mission at a time with one side project. He believes humans are most effective in executing one project at a time. A side project can help him gain new perspectives on the main mission.

Geology graduate student Sean in Arizona tends to devote most of his energy to one large project, but he can become bored and sometimes require a more novel task to keep his attention. He is still learning which work techniques work best for him.

So long as human factors engineer Victor in Texas can balance an efficient schedule and give the necessary attention to each project, he is okay with taking on multiple projects at once. But for day-to-day assignments, he prefers directing his energy and attention toward one thing at a time.

Astrophysics student Xzavier in Florida prefers working on one project at a time so he can give it his 100%. However, as a student he's no stranger to working on several different things at once. Both approaches are manageable and doable for him.

Communicator Brice in Alabama would prefer to work on one project at a time. However, given how connected the world is and how connected he is to the world, he feels an increasing pressure to multitask just to get everything done.

Engineer and world traveler JP prefers working on multiple projects at once. However, it becomes challenging when his plate is overflowing with too much work.

Engineer Lyndsay in Virginia prefers to focus on one project at a time. However, she typically ends up working two or three projects at a time. She regrets when she needs to pass on an opportunity due to her workload.

Engineer Genevieve in Texas prefers to focus on one project at a time. She finds it very difficult to work on multiple projects at once. In the end, she finds it rewarding to see her missions fly after all her hard work.

Despite his varied interests, aerospace engineer Floyd in Iowa prefers to work on one project at a time. He dislikes having to juggle and prioritize between customers or partners when working multiple projects at once. He likes to break one main project into sub-objectives, one for each of the employees under him, so they may focus on one objective at a time as well.

Engineer Paige in California personally finds it most rewarding to focus on one project at a time with a fast turnaround. However, if she was passionate enough about the mission, she could see herself working on a longer-term project. "If I'm really excited and passionate about a project I get consumed by a desire to make it perfect, and other projects become an unwanted distraction."

Astrophysicist Jacob in the United Kingdom prefers to work on one project at a time, focusing on one mission so as not to get distracted and mix up information.

Software engineer Brandon in Washington prefers to work on one project at a time if possible to give himself a better chance to focus. If he must multitask, he prefers to switch tasks on a day-to-day or week-to-week basis.

Astrobiologist Joshua in California prefers to work on one project to completion before moving on. He's more productive when totally immersed in one subject. But he finds himself multitasking out of necessity, forced to switch back and forth between projects. In doing so, it's easy for him to forget important details and lose the thread of what he's trying to accomplish.

From experience, aerospace engineer Logan in Alabama knows that he works best when he can work on one mission at a time. His work often requires a lot of focus. Switching gears can derail his thinking. When working multiple projects, he forgets useful material on one project while pausing to work on something else. He finds he must spend time relearning.

Geomorphology graduate student Stephanie in California prefers to work on one mission at a time. There are so many intricacies within one mission, she explains. She prefers to focus on the details of one mission rather than focusing on many missions and risk missing the details.

Aerospace engineer Anthony in California works best by focusing his attention on a single mission. He prefers to learn the ins and outs of his assignment rather than trying to learn the same amount of material for several projects at once. He believes that focusing on one project at a time allows him to do his job to the best of his ability.

Businesswoman Carolyn in Colorado prefers working on one mission or project at a time to focus on the intricacies and better understand the nuances by immersion in a topic.

Aerospace engineer Yasmin in Florida prefers to work on one mission or project at a time. She enjoys putting all of her focus on one project and being able to steadily work on it.

Aerospace engineer Christopher in Colorado prefers to work on one project at a time to develop a sense of ownership over a single project and connection to a team. He worries that his loyalties are split between two teams when multitasking.

Aerospace engineering student Richard in Washington prefers to work on one mission at a time. Working multiple missions at once in a “touch and go” fashion doesn’t appeal to him. When working on only one mission, he is able to feel ownership over it. This sense of ownership brings him greater satisfaction than having a small impact on multiple missions.

My Juggle

As for me? I laugh because I wrote this entire book while multitasking constantly. It’s a way of life for me. The first time I realized it was unusual to feel so comfortable multitasking was in my childhood when my parents and grandparents expressed astonishment at my ability to hold many instant messaging conversations at one time. The tools have changed but my comfort level hasn't. I switch back and forth between screens and tasks with ease.

As a small business owner and a mother of young children, multitasking is also a necessity for me. I must wear multiple hats and take on many varied tasks. Yet I also feel most alive when doing so. Perhaps I could have written this book more quickly had I not multitasked. Perhaps the writing would be more skilled and eloquent had I been able to focus solely on writing. However, I posit that I would not have been able to write this book at all had I not accomplished my required tasks while concurrently working on this side project. Sometimes multitasking is essential for progress.

Millennial Mixed-taskers

Millennials aren't immune to an increasingly demanding workload and growing expectations that often require working on too many projects at once. Some millennials embrace this challenge, finding multitasking stimulating and exciting. Some millennials would prefer to block out the distractions of multiple items on the to-do list and focus on one project at a time. Rather than a generational preference, multitasking is a personal preference.

CHAPTER 8
CITIZENS OF PLANET EARTH

Globally Connected Millennials

Millennials are the first generation to come of age entirely in the modern internet-connected world. Although the internet traces its origin back to the 1960s, the World Wide Web wasn't established until 1989. Older millennials may remember when personal computers with internet access first appeared in their childhood homes. Younger millennials likely don't remember a time before easy internet access. Mobile cellular phone use increased in the 1990s and smartphones became ubiquitous in the 2010s. Now, the world is always with us, in our pockets or at our fingertips, wherever and whenever we want to connect.

With the ability to communicate with a large percentage of humanity around the world from a very young age, millennials may feel more comfortable communicating internationally. I asked our millennial panel to gauge their comfort level collaborating with international colleagues. Not everyone did so or was able to do so, but almost everyone saw some benefit from collaborating beyond borders. For some, international collaborations in space are not only beneficial, they are essential.

Restricted

Although mechanical engineer Chelsea in Florida has not yet had the opportunity to work with international colleagues, she is eager to branch out someday.

Engineer Nicholas in Texas is happy to share his dreams and aspirations for the future of the new space frontier with everyone and anyone around the globe. However, much of the work he does is restricted, limiting his interactions with international colleagues and the scope of what he can share.

Engineer and CEO Jay in Alabama interacts with many international colleagues regularly, especially on scientific matters. Export control laws limit his ability to collaborate internationally on space technologies, but he enjoys connecting with peers around the globe about his work. He finds diversity and exposure helpful in his own growth. In the United States, the International Traffic in Arms Regulations (ITAR) limit information sharing with international collaborators for many technologies in the aerospace industry.

Aerospace engineer Eric in Alabama commonly works with international colleagues. The aerospace market is international and growing more interconnected every day, he explains. He is careful to work within the legal restrictions of export control.

For biologist David in California, the nature of his work limits his communications with some countries, but otherwise he has no problems collaborating internationally. To be on the safe side, he completely decouples his personal social media sharing from his employer. To not do so would be too easy of a way to get in trouble, he warns.

Engineer Alex in Alabama appreciates international cooperation in space and hopes for a greater U.S. cooperation with international partners, including China. In 2011, Congressman Frank Wolf added language to an appropriations bill[19], commonly known as the Wolf Amendment, restricting NASA's ability to cooperate with China. Currently, NASA may partner with China only if it receives approval from Congress, as China did in 2019 when they used NASA's *Lunar Reconnaissance Orbiter* to monitor the

---

19 United States, Congress, House. Public Law 112-55. *Consolidated and Further Continuing Appropriations Act*, 2012. 112th Congress.

landing of the Chinese *Yutu-2* rover on the far side of the Moon.

A Connected World

Bioengineer Diana in California enthusiastically supports new and growing space agencies around the world. The more players in the field, the more competition to achieve more and perhaps invest more in space programs. She regularly interacts with colleagues at other space agencies around the world. She has run across language barriers and cultural barriers related to sexism, but rarely. Those are the exceptions.

Engineer Altynay in New York perceives the world moving toward globalization. As a member of the Space Generation Advisory Council with ties to the United Nations, she interacts with students and space professionals all around the globe. She and her colleagues regularly communicate on social media platforms and their own private social network. She sees many brilliant minds out there that need the opportunity to realize their dreams. "Work in space broadens our horizons."

Biomedical engineer Jordan in British Columbia is comfortable collaborating with international colleagues. He notes that more and more workplaces, research labs, and hackathons (collaborative programming events) are hosted across borders. We are no longer confined by the walls in which we work, he points out. "More nations getting into space is erasing borders and inspiring new levels of international collaboration."

Through her global internet presence, biology student Skye in Florida interacts with fans internationally. She is not limited by the bounds of her university campus or even her geographic location. Fellow enthusiast from all over the world speak the language of space exploration with her.

Aerospace engineer April in Texas is dedicated to promoting international collaboration in space. She points out the word "international" is in the name of the program she works: *International Space Station*. She regularly interacts with colleagues in Russia and elsewhere. She sees country boundaries and language barriers broken down as all her colleagues work towards the same goals. She believes international collaboration and cooperation are necessary when planning and designing big-ticket space destinations such as space stations and human missions to Mars. Seeing the success of international collaboration every day on the ISS gives her hope for future grand space missions.

Engineer Alex in Georgia is bilingual in English and Spanish and would learn additional languages to communicate with international colleagues. "Part of the beauty of the ISS is that many countries from around the world are able to set aside linguistic and cultural differences to further human advancement."

Mechanical engineer Tracie in Alabama has experience working with international colleagues and presenting at international conferences. In doing so, she was overwhelmed with how broad the space sector is and how many countries participate. She and her international colleagues, "are all on the same team and trying to work toward the same lofty goals (space pun!)."

Corporate communicator Evan in Washington, D.C. believes international collaboration is one of the greatest achievements and benefits of the space program. The diplomacy required to successfully achieve a project like the ISS is nothing short of remarkable in his eyes. He believes we will need a lot more international teamwork if we intend to reach Mars and beyond. In his work, he collaborates with international partners throughout the year.

Engineer Paige in California is inspired by the way the space sector inherently crosses international boundaries. "Anything we send into space travels beyond any one country." She enjoys opportunities to work with international colleagues and uses online connectivity platforms to assist with communication.

Science educator John in Florida is excited about the international aspect of space travel and the space industry. Through his education and his analog space training, he has worked closely with international classmates and colleagues. People everywhere are joining the space industry to further humankind, he explains, and humanity is becoming more dependent on space. With the rise of commercial space ventures, he believes humankind will accomplish some "pretty awesome things" in his lifetime.

Software engineer Brandon in Washington finds camaraderie in sharing stories with fellow space software engineers around the world. "We had a lot of jokes about our common experiences with bureaucracy, engineering culture, and so forth. They're halfway around the world, and even though the language barrier, so much is shared."

Safety engineer Kevin in Florida is comfortable working with his international colleagues in the European Space Agency (ESA). He found it challenging to get past language and cultural differences, but he and his colleagues all have the same goals in mind.

Engineer and businessman Dan in Pennsylvania regularly enjoys communicating with international colleagues. In his role as a business developer, he manifest payments from around the world. It's not uncommon for him to communicate with colleagues from three continents in the same day, he explains. There are frequent opportunities to work with people from diverse cultures who all share a universal passion.

Science reporter Leah in Massachusetts likes to gather multiple perspectives and incorporate them into her work. Communicating and collaborating with international colleagues is essential to gaining these diverse perspectives. She takes care to ensure all potential issues and benefits are considered in her work.

Due to the global nature of his work, satellite engineer Adam in Colorado frequently collaborates with international colleagues. He enjoys learning about different approaches and working through problems with people of diverse backgrounds.

Businesswoman Carolyn in Colorado not only is very comfortable interacting with international colleagues, she treasures the global focus of her work. Although communicating effectively with international colleagues can be difficult at times, in her opinion, it's always worth the effort and provides her with better results.

Businesswoman Crystal in Texas regularly communicates with international colleagues. She enjoys the learning experience and the broader perspective of activities and ideas. She delights in others' cultural holiday celebrations.

Having grown up in a major international city, human factors engineer Victor in Texas loves interacting with individuals from other countries. He gains insights on how to solve problems from a different point of view. He also appreciates gaining new perspectives on life and the world. He believes we all gain from becoming increasingly tolerant of differences and learning about other cultures and beliefs. If there's a will, in his experience, the language barrier can be overcome.

Engineer Genevieve in Texas is thankful to live in a society that supports space exploration and continues to reach beyond. She is especially thankful for the successful international collaboration of the ISS, an accomplishment of so many countries and cultures assembling a laboratory in space together. She feels fortunate to have worked closely with Russian colleagues which allowed her to learn how another culture views spaceflight.

Physicist Lindsey in Maryland has a desire to collaborate with international colleagues which has fueled her passion to learn Russian. Speaking with Russian scientist was one of the most incredible parts of her study abroad experience in Moscow. She hopes to tackle German and French next. Through the Space Generation Advisory Council, she feels connected with space professionals across the globe. Nothing energizes her more than a feeling of sharing a common passion for space with other people across the globe from entirely different cultural backgrounds and professional specialties.

In his job working on the ISS program, aerospace engineer Mason in Alabama communicates and collaborates with international colleagues regularly. Every international interaction he's ever had has been very rewarding. He's had the pleasure of working with some very skilled people around the world. He admits his appreciation that English is the primary language used in the field.

Engineer Rachel in Florida has the benefit of being a native English speaker in an English-speaking country. She marvels at and appreciates the way her foreign colleagues understand and speak English so well, although accents can be tricky, she admits. She cringes at the awkwardness when she needs to ask people to repeat themselves (and still may not understand the second time). Email and text chat help with the communication barrier.

In her work on the ISS program, engineer Lindsay in Alabama has gotten to hear some pretty neat stories from her international colleagues. Collaborating with international partners helps her to grow personally and professionally as she works on becoming more comfortable speaking with people she doesn't know very well.

As a scientist, Eddie in California appreciates the wide array of resources his international colleagues contribute to science. "We have more to gain from cooperation than competition from our international colleagues," especially given the specialized knowledge necessary for scientific instrumentation and other specific technical areas.

Science knows no bounds, especially not sovereign bounds and international borders. Astrobiologist Marie in California doesn't know how she could advance her research without her international colleagues. From North America she communicates with colleagues on at least four continents weekly: South America, Europe, Asia, and her own. She finds coordinating meetings over multiple times zones difficult but appreciates the timing of emails. She communicates with European colleagues in the morning and Asian colleagues in the evening. Scientific conferences are by their nature international with scientists from various countries traveling all over the world.

Much of the work engineer and data scientist Nikolai in the Czech Republic is involved with is international. He has business ties to the United States, India, and the Czech Republic. One of his most earnest efforts is increasing awareness and motivation within the United States to work with developing space startups internationally. Space is truly an international effort requiring input from every nation, he asserts, even the little ones.

Nikolai tries to keep a flexible schedule to work with colleagues in multiple time zones, but he feels limited, especially when scheduling business calls. He prefers in-person meetings and video chats, but scheduling is always a challenge. He uses text messages as a quick and easy way to schedule calls and meetings. Email gets around most of the time zone problems, but he feels frustrated by his inability to communicate complex ideas through brief written messages.

Communicator Brice in Alabama enjoys working with international colleagues and does so daily through teleconferencing and email.

Engineer and CEO Mark in Kentucky regularly communicates and collaborates with international colleagues. Almost daily he works with colleagues in Europe and Asia from his office in North America.

CEO Scott in Florida is extremely comfortable collaborating with international colleagues. In fact, he encourages it. He speaks with colleagues all over the world from a multitude of countries

Astronomer Crystal in Maryland regularly communicates with scientists from all around the world to prepare their missions for spaceflight.

Engineer Lyndsay in Virginia has served as an international relations officer of a nonprofit organization that deals primarily with international collaboration. In this position, she interacted with international colleagues on a daily basis and thoroughly enjoyed it.

Space policy professional Nate in Washington, DC enjoys working with colleagues from all over the world, though he doesn't get to collaborate internationally as much as he'd like. He enjoys face-to-face meetings when feasible.

As a scientist, Ryan in Colorado is accustomed to working with international colleagues, including students and visiting scholars.

Astrophysics student Xzavier in Florida regularly interacts with international classmates. His university has a high international student population. He has no problem talking with and collaborating with anyone of any nationality.

As a Brazilian living and working in Florida, aerospace engineer Thais is very comfortable interacting with international colleagues. Unfortunately, she does not get to do this regularly for work. But she does interact with her family in Brazil frequently.

Aerospace engineer Darius in Alabama is envious of his colleagues who have the opportunity to travel the world for work. He enjoys working with international colleagues and hopes to have the opportunity to expand his international interactions in the future.

One Planet

Engineer Nicholas may live in Washington, but he is a man of the world. We are all citizens of Earth, sharing this planet with 7.5 billion other humans of diverse experiences and perspectives. He embraces us in all our differences, disagreements, and cultural clashes.

Nicholas rejects physical limits. The Earth may be 25,000 miles or 40,000 kilometers around, but the people and knowledge of the world are at our fingertips. Does his friend live a continent away? No problem. Millennials grew up as the internet matured. We are more connected now than ever. He uses Skype, Google Hangouts, and social media to easily connect with his fellow travelers on Spaceship Earth.

The co-mingling of new ideas and diverse perspectives is a value Nicholas will take with him to the stars. His mind is open, delighting in any new, well-reasoned perspective he had never previously considered. Often these refreshing points of view are creations of cultural differences, a natural consequence of the diversity of life experiences, he explains. How different will the life experiences of future space settlers be from our own? he wonders. What new ideas and refreshing perspectives will be created within the human mind from the social expansion that follows from the physical expansion of the human experience?

Aerospace engineer and businessman Ethan in Alabama envisions a path to developing a spacefaring society that is only accomplished through international cooperation. He believes we can build upon the successful example of commercial aviation.

Astronomy graduate student Jessica in Alabama welcomes interacting with her international classmates and colleagues. "My utopia would be a world where nations collaborated for the sole purpose of space endeavors." There's little land on Earth left to explore and conquer, so she believes nations should work together globally to discover what is beyond. She hopes humanity can also work together to take steps to protect what we have left on our planet.

One of the primary reasons aerospace engineer Yasmin in Florida decided to pursue a career in space was to work with international partners. Interactions with international colleagues allow international partnerships to grow, she explains. She dreams of a type of global peace stemming from these efforts. Space is a frontier that she hopes the inhabitants of Planet Earth can explore together.

I, too, feel comfortable as a citizen of Planet Earth. I interact with thousands of people across the globe, usually unaware of their geographical locations, sometimes considering that they are likely unaware of my location as well. My business has no boundaries and several of my clients are international. While I am undoubtedly culturally American as well as American by birth and citizenship, I do not consider space the domain of any dominant nation. As the plaque created by American government agency NASA and left on the lunar surface by the American *Apollo 11* astronauts in 1969 states, "We came in peace for all mankind."

Millennials of the World Unite

While some millennials are restricted from interacting with international colleagues due to company or legal restrictions, millennials universally support collaborating internationally. Even millennials who do not yet work with international colleagues hope to do so in the future. Millennials in the space sector are more inclined to see their work as inherently international and less likely to express nationalistic motivations for their work. "American leadership" and "America first" are common phrases in U.S. government and space leadership, but much less likely to be spoken by millennials. Many millennials hope space exploration unifies nations to work together as we progress outward representing planet Earth.

Chapter 9
Social Media Mavens

Millennials on Social Media

A series of networked computers connecting users with similar interests around the world naturally led to a new way to be social in the digital world. Early bulletin board systems, chat rooms, and messaging tools in the 1980s and 90s laid the foundation for modern-day social media platforms. Facebook and Myspace developed the first iterations of their websites in 2003. The youngest millennials have never known a world without social media platforms allowing users to share and interact with content through networks of their peers.

Today, there are dozens, perhaps hundreds of social media websites and tools. According to Facebook, 2.45 billion users log onto its platform every month. If that figure is accurate, it represents almost a third of the population of the planet. Millennials are the largest users of Facebook according to their demographic information. For millennial users, YouTube, WhatsApp, Instagram, Snapchat, and Twitter are also popular choices.

I asked our millennial panel about their social media use and their comfort level using social media. I also wanted to know if they felt comfortable collaborating with colleagues over social media.

A Preference for Privacy

Aerospace engineer Floyd in Iowa is uncomfortable using social media entirely and doesn't touch it. "I feel that social media was a mistake. An unavoidable mistake, but a mistake nonetheless." Yet he admits this opinion is probably in the minority, especially among his and younger generations. For better or for worse, social media is here to stay, but he chooses not to participate in it.

Space policy professional Nate in Washington, DC finds social media to be invasive and more of a chore. Therefore, he chooses not to participate as much as most of his fellow millennials. He does not find it enjoyable.

Engineer Vito in Colorado prefers face-to-face communication. Body language is essential in communication, he explains. When that isn't possible, he prefers email. He believes social media hampers our ability to fully communicate with each other. In most cases, we cannot read body language in social media communications.

Engineer and CEO Jay in Alabama is not comfortable communicating with colleagues via social media. He prefers to call or meet in person to work. He believes in-person or phone conversations nurture relationships in a way social media can't. "I have to look them in the eye or let them hear my voice."

Aerospace engineer Yasmin in Florida prefers human interactions or private communication methods such as email, video chat, and phone calls. She is not particularly fond of social media due to the lack of security. She sees other means of communication to be more secure.

Astrobiologist Joshua in California easily converses with colleagues anywhere in the world. He prefers communicating on an individual basis rather than *en masse*. He dislikes social media and feels uncomfortable with anyone knowing the details of his personal life. He worries that kind of openness will negatively impact job applications and grant proposals. Many hiring managers and selection committees look up candidates and proposers on social media platforms to access freely available information not included in their applications and proposals. Joshua values his privacy.

Engineer Justin in Florida isn't comfortable communicating with colleagues over social media. Although he thinks social media is a powerful tool, he does not think it's a good idea to share technical information on those platforms.

Engineer Tom in Florida admits that his workplace is more sensitive to national security concerns, limiting his contact with foreign nationals. He avoids social media just to be on the safe side. By its nature, social media is global and users are not limited to the bounds of one nation.

Engineer and CEO Mark in Kentucky doesn't communicate on social media personally, but he directs his company to do so. Whereas some companies have a minimal or no internet presence, other companies have embraced social media as a means of information sharing, marketing, branding, and consumer feedback.

Scientist Amy in Virginia embraces new technology but her job advocates caution with outside communication. She finds it extremely difficult to have relationships with international colleagues due to ITAR restrictions. She only uses social media for personal use and never at work. She feels it's safer that way. She'd rather err on the side of caution with ITAR-sensitive information.

Due to the nature of his work, aerospace engineer Darius in Alabama isn't comfortable using social media to communicate with coworkers about work. He cannot discuss sensitive information and technical details in public forums. Instead, he uses social media to communicate with coworkers socially.

Engineer Genevieve in Texas reserves social media for interacting with friends only. Much of her work is proprietary so it doesn't make sense to her to communicate technical information over social media. Despite the limitations in what she can share, she does use social media for networking.

Student and museum tour guide Walter in Florida isn't comfortable using social media for work purposes. He prefers the privacy of email and video chatting platforms. However, he sometimes posts space-related information on social media to keep his friends and family informed.

Satellite engineer Adam in Colorado is pleased to call some of his coworkers friends. He enjoys communicating with them and other friends over social media, but prefers not to discuss business so publicly.

Communicator Brice in Alabama prefers to use most social media for non-work communications, restricting work communications to work-centric social media platforms such as Slack.

Mechanical engineer Chelsea in Florida enjoys connecting with friends over social media, but she keeps personal life and work life separate. Although she is friends with some of her colleagues, she's uncomfortable discussing work-related topics over social media platforms. She prefers the separation of those areas of her life.

Aerospace engineer Logan in Alabama uses social media frequently but only for his personal life. He tries to keep his personal life separate from his work life.

Diversity is important to software manager Sarah in New Hampshire. Bringing together people of diverse backgrounds with different perspectives is something she values in a collaboration. However, she does not do this on social media, not professionally at least. She reserves her social media interactions for a small group of friends as a way to let down her guard and relax from the expectations of work. She prefers the organization and simplicity of email as the most effective way to communicate with her colleagues.

CEO Scott in Florida speaks with colleagues over social media platforms but not about work. He prefers to keep a strict personal and professional barrier. He feels that work-related matters should be left to email or phone calls.

Bioengineer Diana in California does not feel comfortable using social media to exchange scientific information. She is frustrated by the lack of clarity and the misinformation she encounters when communicating over social media platforms, equating it to a game of "telephone" where messages get garbled from incomplete interpretations. However, she does use social media to communicate with friends.

Astrobiologist Marie in California appreciates social media for casually keeping track of friends and colleagues and for publicizing her own work, but admits she prefers email. Social media is inherently public. The real work is done in private messages, she states. Research that is not yet public needs to be kept within a limited circle of contacts best communicated with by email or teleconferencing, she explains.

Public Engagement

Aerospace engineer and businessman Ethan in Alabama collaborates with colleagues through social media. He uses video chatting and instant messaging tools to accelerate the pace of project development. He runs working groups through social media platforms. Social media has become a way for him to effectively communicate with colleagues remotely.

As a communications professional, corporate communicator Evan in Washington, DC likes to say, "I tweet for a living!" Many companies have incorporated social media into their corporate communications strategy. Some companies and organizations have dedicated social media managers and teams who specialize in communicating best with the unique cultures and demographics of each social media platform in producing content exclusively for social media audiences.

Millennials are sometimes given the keys to social media accounts because they are viewed as children of the digital age. Engineer and executive Justin in Florida recalls a time when he was asked to create a Twitter account for his team, administer it, and even coordinate with other social media teams. It wasn't long before he was asked to give lunch workshops on how to effectively engage the public on social media. He was assigned to assist with his team's website to help drive engagement because he was seen to have the "pulse" of the group's users. He believes he was chosen to promote the mission of his team in a way that was faster, more effective, and more broadly viewed than traditional messaging.

Engineer Hayley in California is very comfortable communicating and collaborating over social media. She has experience managing team social media accounts. She uses Twitter especially to reach out to professors and professionals about space issues and to stay in the know.

Social media is how aerospace engineer Mason in Alabama keeps his finger on the pulse of the space industry. Whether it's catching up on space news, following a friend's space business, or sharing jokes and pictures with his coworkers, social media makes the space community feel like family. When you know someone, it's easier to work with them, he explains.

Geodesist Ryan in Colorado uses Instagram and Facebook in his personal time. He uses social media to socialize with colleagues and keep up with newsworthy developments in his field. But he doesn't find social media to be an ideal channel for communicating technical information. He prefers face-to-face interactions augmented by visual aids to be the most effective way for him to collaborate. His preferred method for communicating remotely is email. To discuss information in real time, he uses video chatting and phone calls.

Aerospace engineer Christopher in Colorado uses LinkedIn and Facebook to connect with colleagues. While email is his primary method of communication, he appreciates LinkedIn especially as a great way to stay in touch with colleagues he meets at conferences and other business trips.

Physicist Lindsey in Maryland keeps in touch with fellow NASA interns, Space Generation Advisory Council members, and university engineering club members on Facebook as well as through email and text messaging. However, she considers herself more of a private individual who prefers not to showcase her life on social media.

Engineer Paige in California finds Facebook, LinkedIn, and messaging apps particularly useful for her collaborations. Similarly, astronomy graduate student Jessica in Alabama finds networking in astronomy to be easy and efficient through social media.

Engineer and data scientist Nikolai in the Czech Republic enjoys using social media for introductions and more casual conversations. Social media has been a successful part of his business strategy, landing him a couple contracts he doesn't think would have been possible without the use of social media platforms' algorithms working in his favor. He uses software tools for teamwork but finds them lacking.

Science reporter Leah in Massachusetts has built a community on social media which helps her to gain a diversity of perspectives. Through social media, she can communicate with scientist, find the right person to help with her work or answer a question, and reach out to others who might not otherwise be available or easy to contact.

Astrobiologist Eddie in California uses social media to promote preliminary scientific results and papers to a broader audience beyond his immediate colleagues and those in specialized fields. He also appreciates the advice he can solicit from other scientists on social media and the opportunities social media can provide. But like any communication medium, social media can be abused. He takes care to be considerate and thoughtful when communicating on these platforms.

Engineer Alex in Alabama enjoys communicating with anyone about space and his work. He cultivates his social media experience to learn from space industry professionals and communicate technically online.

Aviator Christopher in Florida uses social media to connect with international colleagues who share the same interests. They put aside geopolitical differences and focus on science. He communicates broad ideas via social media but prefers to save more important discussions for email.

Biomedical engineer Jordan in British Columbia is happy to play a small role in science education and communication on social media. "The power of social media connects us to millions of people with similar interests, allows us to connect on shared problems, and solve problems virtually."

Businesswoman Crystal in Texas enjoys using social media to connect with people far beyond her physical reach and strike up conversations with people of different perspectives. "Social media can be a great learning experience, and make you feel like you're connecting with people even though they are not physically present." However, she prefers face-to-face communication. She feels she must overcompensate when communicating through text to ensure that her ideas and tone come through clearly.

While biology student Skye in Florida is studying for her degree, she is taking full advantage of opportunities that involve her in the field she loves. She is an avid social media user. Her Instagram account has thousands of followers dreaming about space exploration with her. She has since expanded to multiple social media platforms and has her own informational website on space.

Businessman Barry in Florida believes the best way to go deeper into space is through international effort and partnership. He communicates worldwide on Twitter, enjoying promoting space but being cautious not to reveal sensitive information.

Barry is inspired by the connectivity of millennials. Through social media, ideas can be exchanged and subject popularity can be measured like never before. As it turns out, NASA and spaceflight are very popular subjects.

Engineer Nathan in Colorado doesn't personally communicate with colleagues over social media, but he would like to. Science is meant to be shared and cross-checked, he explains. He would want to share whatever accomplishments or questions he had with as many people as possible through social media.

Astronomer Rodrigo in New York shares science results

on social media, specifically on Facebook. But he doesn't do collaborative work over social media.

Aerospace engineer Eric in Alabama regularly uses social media for public discussions such as celebrating space and professional accomplishments. He prefers email for business or technical collaborations.

Engineer Nicholas in Texas is cautious on social media, taking care not to write or share anything sensitive or proprietary. He mainly uses social media to spread his passion for space, not to discuss specific work topics.

Mechanical engineer Tracie in Alabama is very public about her work on social media. She's so passionate about what she does, she finds it hard not to share. She feels fortunate that NASA is one of the most open government organizations regarding sharing information. She believes that by sharing her work on social media, she helps to inspire the next generation of scientists and engineers.

Business consultant Liam in Virginia has expertise in information technology, business, and space educational outreach. Much of his work in the space sector is science communication. Social media is the lifeblood of his work. Communicating with his fellows anywhere on this wide planet is second nature to him.

Planetary scientist Kelsi in Colorado doesn't use social media often, but she recognizes it as a useful tool in her field. For example, if she is unable to attend a conference, she can read about the conference on her Twitter feed to get some idea of the happenings.

Engineer and businessman Dan in Pennsylvania appreciate those who take the time to share great content on social media. He doesn't write content himself. He admits it's a very time-consuming activity just to keep up with the news on social media.

Design engineer Rachel in Florida sees the value in social media for communicating with and informing the public, but she doesn't use it herself anymore. She doesn't feel the need to use social internet platforms to keep in touch with those close to her. Social media isn't useful for the kinds of collaborations she does.

Engineer Mark in Virginia enjoys communicating via social media. It's his main form of communication these days.

Human factors engineer Victor in Texas believes face-to-face interactions are the most information-rich method of interpersonal communication. "However in this day and age, communication via social media is not only becoming increasingly common, but also imperative to the success of groups, organizations, and companies. As a millennial, I find it almost obligatory to not only be comfortable with social media communication, but to master it as well." He quotes the saying, "Get with the times or get left behind."

I am a self-professed social media addict. I delight in sharing my love of space and other topics with a worldwide audience. The space community I've found on social media, especially Twitter, keeps me motivated, informed, inspired, and grounded. I spend hours each day keeping informed about space happenings from news organizations, space journalists, company and organization accounts, and individuals. In turn, I also help spread information about what I'm doing and learning. Live tweeting conferences and events, that is, posting about an event as it's happening, is an especially useful way to spread information within a social media community in real time.

However, being so public on social media isn't without its risks. I mostly keep my personal life restricted to friends-only social media interactions. My public business and science communications opens me up to criticisms, trolls, and misogynistic attacks. However, most of the time I am able to cultivate my social media experience to feel a true sense of community and camaraderie with space colleagues, acquaintances, and friends online.

As a small business owner, I see the benefit to using social media to promote my business. I have yet to pay for marketing. Instead, I let sharing of organic social media content sharing to work in my favor. I also help run the social media accounts for a couple space conferences and have seen a similar benefit from spreading the word through user sharing and interactions.

I have also seen the downside: unwarranted targeted attacks against organizations and individuals with no consequences for the harassers. Divisive and abusive behavior on social media is widespread, sometimes by real users and sometimes by programmed "bots." The spread of misinformation or "fake news" has also become a real issue with true repercussions. In many ways, social media is still in its infancy with many improvements to be made before it's a safe and effective means of peer social networking and information sharing.

There's no denying the power of social media to bring together a group of people for a common purpose. I rely on social media for networking, staying informed, and bouncing around ideas. I first proposed the concept for this book on Twitter, and after getting positive feedback and interest, decided to pursue the project. I've seen careers started, supported, enhanced, and guided on social media within the space community, including my own. Despite the abuse by outsiders, there is a strong sisterhood of young women in space supporting and uplifting each other via social media platforms. Social media interactions have the potential to change lives and move the world, one individual at a time.

Social Media for Some

Does the prevalence of social media use among millennials translate to widespread comfort with social media? If our millennial panel is any indication: no. Many millennials are private social media users and prefer to keep their information out of the public eye. Some cannot share details about their work because of the nature of their business. Some have strict barriers between what they share with their friends and family and what they share with their coworkers. Some enjoy using social media for science communication but keep their private lives to themselves. Some are uncomfortable using social media altogether, valuing their privacy above all. Some embrace the openness and transparency of social media. Millennials may have come of age with social media, but their usage varies widely.

CHAPTER 10
TALKING ABOUT MY GENERATION

Generational Differences

A generation is a product of its time. Culture, technology, and major world events help shape a collective's mutual formative experiences. A cohort of people born around the same time will experience similar cultural norms, technological evolution, historical events, economic cycles, and pop culture trends. Values change, demographics change, priorities change, opportunities change. Experiences will differ with factors such as geographic location, language, family, race and ethnicity, religion, class, sexuality, politics, and other life experiences. When we speak of a generation as a collective, we generalize. We simplify. We make assumptions. We form judgments about ourselves, our similarly aged peers, as well as the generations before and after us. Somewhere in those observations, we uncover some truths.

Many of the differences in generations can be attributed to age and stage of life. A college student will have a different perspective than a retiree no matter what generation they each belong to. A parent of an infant will have a different perspective than an empty-nester. An entry-level employee will have a different perspective than an executive. Our millennial panel includes students and CEOs along with a diversity of life experiences.

I asked our millennial panel whether they feel that their millennial peers have different priorities, opinions, and/or values than their older colleagues, and if so, in what ways they believe the generations differ.

I encourage this chapter in particular to be read with an open mind. Not every viewpoint will speak to you. You may view some of these statements as untrue to your worldview, unfair to your generation, or contradictory to your life experiences. To the panelists opening themselves up to your scrutiny, these statements are true to their worldview, fair to their generation the way they see it, and honor their life experiences. Opinions on generational differences can be contradictory and still be valid and worthy of consideration.

Intergenerational Learning

Businesswoman Carolyn in Colorado believes the differences between generations have more to do with age. Her older colleagues may have different priorities, opinions, and values regarding risk, economics, and government or military involvement in space based on decades of experience in the industry. "If we look back to the engineers and scientists involved in the Apollo program, I think they would be quite similar to today's young workforce."

Not having a family himself, engineer and data scientist Nikolai in the Czech Republic wonders if his older colleagues have less time to work due to family and other commitments. He also believes older colleagues may weigh job security and financial safety higher than he does as a young millennial.

However, Nikolai doesn't see differences in the generations. He believes we are all working in this industry to push forward the frontier, regardless of our age. Older colleagues may have memories of Mercury, Gemini, and Apollo, and through those achievements, a sense of national camaraderie they built their careers on. Millennials may not have experienced that history personally but they have the same drive to push forward to exceed half-century-old ambitions that haven't yet quite become reality.

Astrophysicist Jacob in the United Kingdom doesn't see any real differences in priorities, opinions, or values between the generations. He believes his mentors have a similar outlook as he does on the balance between scientific progress and risk-taking. He hopes his older colleagues feel the same way.

When engineer Paige in California was a child, science fiction stories such as *Star Trek* inflamed her passion for space. Now, as a young adult, she thinks there is nothing cooler than being paid to send things into space. She asserts the drive to explore the unknown is within all generations of people. There may be differences between the generations, she admits, but people involved in space exploration are in it for very similar reasons regardless of their age.

Engineer and CEO Jay in Alabama believes that fundamentally, millennials have similar priorities, opinions, and values compared to other generations. He doesn't believe people are defined by their generation. "One's generation doesn't reflect the totality of an individual." He respects his older colleagues for their experience.

Launch and landing engineer Adam in Florida appreciates and respects the knowledge and experience of his older colleagues. He has watched some of his millennial peers wasting time and effort reinventing a "square wheel" rather than picking up the round wheel that older generations have already invented. "Pick up the round one they handed you and figure out how to make it go faster and last longer." He has learned a lot from his later career colleagues and their decades of experience.

Engineer Genevieve in Texas values the many years of experience her older colleagues bring to the table. She believes her millennial coworkers need to learn from the experience of their older coworkers before considering a new solution or approach of their own invention. She advises her millennial colleagues to focus on gaining technical experience before attempting to be too innovative.

Human factors engineer Victor in Texas strongly respects and admires his older colleagues who take the time to teach and train new members of the industry. He believes they are motivated by a desire to prevent millennials from making the same mistakes so we can further progress the work that has already been accomplished.

Aerospace engineer Darius in Alabama appreciates the experience of his older colleagues. He sees many millennials struggle through challenges their older coworkers have previously struggled through. He believes there is a great learning opportunity for millennials to work with older generations. He admires the amount of knowledge his older, experienced colleagues have. He's thankful to work with and learn from them. He knows he can always turn to them for help.

Generational Shifts

The older generations bring experience to the table that he and his fellow millennials don't have, aerospace engineer Floyd in Iowa explains. They have seen successes and failures that have changed the way they look at their work and the world, he adds. He believes past failures added up to demotivate and demoralize his older colleagues to the point where they give up on their dreams of great space legacies and instead pursue careers for profit or to just make a living.

Floyd wonders if his older colleagues are more closed-minded. Or perhaps millennials are more open-minded. His experience has shown him that millennials tend to have conversations about more challenging technical topics whereas older colleagues tend to dismiss them out of hand. It's unclear to him whether this is a generational difference or simply an age difference, with older colleagues having more experience and perspective than younger colleagues to know what is realistic and what isn't.

Aviator Christopher in Florida values the maturity of his older colleagues. They usually have more realistic views of what can and cannot be done, he explains.

Engineer Kyle in Washington sees the millennial generation as "more willing to spend time and resources on things those with more industry experience would deem impossible." He cites SpaceX's younger workforce as a key to their success. Young employees have not yet learned what is "impossible," he explains. As a result, he believes the space industry has been fundamentally changed because of the can-do approach of millennials. At the same time, he also sees the value in older, experienced space professionals balancing the optimism of their less experienced younger coworkers.

Engineer and CEO Mark in Kentucky sees a difference in the risk tolerances between millennials and older generations. He values the beginner's mind as an asset to pursue endeavors that he admits most reasonable people wouldn't do.

Mechanical engineer Tracie in Alabama feels millennials are more optimistic than older generations. Perhaps because millennials haven't been in the workforce long enough to work on a project that is later canceled or become passionate about a project that never comes to fruition, she ponders. She is inspired by her peers wearing SpaceX "Occupy Mars" t-shirts because they truly believe human settlements on Mars are an achievable goal and they themselves will have a role in it. Contrary to popular stereotypes, she believes millennials are task-oriented. If she has to work in the evening or on vacation to prepare a report or dial into a call, she will do so to benefit her team.

Safety engineer Kevin in Florida has noticed his older colleagues seem more resistant to change. Millennials are willing to go out of their comfort zone and try different things more readily than older generations who typically want to continue to do things they are used to doing, he observes.

Aerospace engineer Logan in Alabama has observed his older colleagues have a mentality of, "We can't do it like that, we've always done it this way." Whereas he and his millennial peers investigate novel methods and ideas to solve problems.

Astrobiologist Joshua in California is optimistic about the future of the space sector. He believes most of his millennial colleagues are optimistic as well, more so than his older colleagues. Or perhaps millennials are more open to discussing and sharing their optimism, he suggests.

Biology student Skye in Florida sees a changing world continuing to expand and grow. The opportunities today are endless. She believes millennials' priorities, opinions, and values are much more open. Millennials have the freedom to make more decisions that benefit them as a generation, she explains. The way she sees it, each and every generation has greater opportunities. It's up to each individual to act on them.

Engineer Mark in Virginia sees many of his older colleagues content with the pace of progress. He feels they seem almost complacent now having done their great work in the past. Some of his older colleagues even seem to impede progress, he observes.

Aerospace engineer Kelly in Florida believes millennials have a fast-paced, high-stress, let's-get-things-done mentality. In her experience, millennials want to work their fastest with high coffee intake and little sleep. She admits millennials may overlook details due to lack of experience. Her older colleagues may move at a slower pace, but she believes they value quality over deadlines.

Mechanical engineer Chelsea in Florida wonders if perhaps pride in their work is why she perceives her older colleagues seem to lack work-life balance. Many of her older colleagues take few or no vacations. Some even lose unused accrued vacation time from the lack of desire to get away from work. She doesn't see that same kind of work obsession in her millennial colleagues. She and her peers like to work hard, but they also like to go home and have a life separate from work.

Aerospace engineer Mason in Alabama believes millennials prioritize career advancement more than older generations have. Some of his older colleagues are very happy to continue in their current positions with no plans for advancement. Millennials also expect to be rewarded for their hard work and dedication, he states. He observes some of his older colleagues valuing hard work regardless of the reward. In general, millennials are not a generation of workaholics, he explains. He believes work-life balance is a must for millennials. He has seen any disruption to that balance negatively impact personal lives. He believes millennials will choose family and life balance over work every time. Finally, he observes millennials to be more open-minded to change in the workplace and will adapt to technology more quickly and intuitively than older generations do.

Despite his big dreams, engineer Tom in Florida wonders if there is a lack of passion within his generation. He sees how the workforce has changed. Employees are no longer loyal to employers for decades. And employers are no longer loyal to employees, eliminating pensions and other benefits and cutting back programs which disproportionately affect younger workers. Employees easily hop from job to job within similar companies, further eroding the sense of loyalty to one employer. Tom wonders if this new workplace reality combined with what's now seen as routine rocket launches have dampened millennials' dedication to the space sector.

Aerospace engineer April in Texas observes older generations rely more on seniority whereas her generation is breaking down some of those hierarchical traditions. She believes millennials place more value on efficiency and matching skill sets to the right job, regardless of seniority. She also sees millennials moving away from the standard 40-hour work week and more toward a flexible but efficient schedule.

Millennials grew up in the internet age where everything is so visibly interconnected. Science reporter Leah in Massachusetts believes this global perspective contributes to millennials leaning toward more progressive values. She and some of her millennial friends and colleagues put less trust in traditional career paths, problem solving, and personal life. "We tend to seek solutions beyond the status quo, because within it many of us would have to work twice as hard as the previous generation did to obtain the same stability, prestige, and professional/personal freedom."

Astronomer Brett in Queensland believes millennials are more connected than older generations thanks to new technology. He believes this connectivity enables millennials to care more about their fellow humans globally and about our impact on the environment.

Design engineer Rachel in Florida see value in her own dissatisfaction and impatience. Broadly speaking, she believes millennials are more impatient than older generations. She sees millennials having more of a drive to see change happen more quickly. "I've also noticed the older generation is much more comfortable with control and patriarchy, whereas my generation wants more autonomy and independence." Cultural change takes trust and strong communication, but she believes we are getting there. She sees that cultural change happening within NASA as well, which will only encourage more creativity and progress within the space sector.

Engineering student Amoree in Georgia believes millennials value diversity increasingly more than previous generations have. She observes the space sector changing to welcome more women and minorities. She attributes this change to the millennial generation growing up with social media with increased ability and willingness to express themselves and reach out to others.

Engineer Nicholas in Washington credits his upbringing for his idealism and liberal values. Messages of tolerance and sustainability preached within TV shows such as *Barney*[20] and *Captain Planet*[21] are evidence of the social changes in his generation, he says. He sees these core values bringing about social changes that are increasingly supported by millennials.

Space policy professional Nate in Washington, DC be-

20 *Barney & Friends*. PBS. Premiered 6 April, 1992.

21 *Captain Planet and the Planeteers*. TBS. Premiered 15 September 15 1990. *The New Adventures of Captain Planet*. TBS. Premiered 11 September, 1993.

lieves collaboration and collective decision-making are values millennials uphold more than previous generations. Inclusivity is also an important value to him. He envisions society's various players expanding into space in new ways in the coming decades.

Astronomer and astrobiologist Giada in Maryland has noticed millennials tend to be willing to support diversity and inclusiveness initiatives more than older generations do. She see millennials making these issues explicit priorities. She points to the graduate student-led Diversity Journal Club in her graduate program has an example of an initiative to welcome underrepresented minorities in astronomy.

Planetary scientist Kelsi in Colorado observes millennials promoting diversity more than previous generations. "I feel very strongly that diversity of workforce will lead to diversity of thought, which can only be a good thing for any scientific or exploration endeavor."

Businesswoman Crystal in Texas sees a difference in the way millennials value diversity and emotional intelligence compared to older generations. She sees millennials tending to look for employers who care about the environment, human rights, and animal rights. She appreciates her older colleagues for the vast amount of knowledge and experience they pass down concerning career advice, perseverance, and work ethic. However, she struggles with certain biases in older colleagues. "There is still an excessive amount of sexism and they simply don't understand that they're doing anything inappropriate." She believes older colleagues tend to fear or misunderstand technology and shy away from technological solutions that would help them in the workplace. "They don't understand how much easier their job would be if they took the time to learn how to utilize the technology provided to them to its fullest intent." She believes millennials and older generations have a lot to learn from each other.

Scientist Amy in Virginia believes she and her millennial colleagues are more adaptable with new computer-based tools and applications compared to older generations.

Planetary scientist Ryan in Missouri believes older and younger generations want a lot of the same things, but millennials and younger generations are willing to take more risks. Millennials didn't have the benefit of living through Apollo. "Millenials want our own 'Apollo' and we are willing to take the necessary risks to get there." She also sees millennials prioritizing diversity such as increased involvement by women and minorities.

Aerospace engineer and businessman Ethan in Alabama views his colleagues in three generational ranges: The Apollo Generation, the Space Shuttle Generation, and what he calls the Curiosity Generation. The way he sees it, the Apollo Generation of the early space program was motivated by national pride to win the Cold War. The Space Shuttle Generation, which may include some older millennials, was motivated by scientific research and international cooperation. The Curiosity Generation, which may include younger millennials and generation Z, is motivated by a desire to travel to or interact with space personally and increased international cooperation. He believes millennials will continue to develop a sustained human presence in space for peaceful purposes.

President John F. Kennedy posed the challenge, "Ask not what your country can do for you – ask what you can do for your country."[22] Businessman Barry in Florida is inspired by that sentiment to work as hard as he can for his country's space program. Yet he worries this sentiment is not shared by others of his generation.

Aerospace engineer Eric in Alabama sees a differences in what generations value. Older generations valued national pride when it came to space accomplishments. He sees millennials valuing corporate and personal pride over national pride.

As student and museum tour guide Walter in Florida sees it, millennials "grew up in an era where spaceflight has cemented its place in humanity. Now I think we all want to see it move into a new era where we expand beyond Earth, and at the same time exploit space to improve our life on Earth."

For software manager Sarah in New Hampshire, one goal is common to her colleagues and herself: extending farther into the Universe by creating infrastructure to live and work in space. However, she sees significant differences in how her older colleagues view this goal. Space

---

22 Kennedy, John F. "John F. Kennedy's Inaugural Address." 20 January, 1961, Washington, D.C.

efforts in the United States from the start of the space age were intent on beating the Soviet Union and forming international cooperation and peace.

Sarah believes millennials are more likely to see space as being the final frontier of exploration and not a place of political or geopolitical gain. Millennials want to push the limits of our predecessors and create a new era of space, she continues, one that has no bounds or fears, and one that is built on international cooperation from the start. With the rise of technology connecting the globe, she believes international collaboration is even more of a reality, perhaps even a necessity.

Aerospace engineer Thais in Florida has observed her older colleagues reminiscing about the "Shuttle days." She and her millennial peers are ready to move forward to land humans on Mars, she declares. She is envious of those able to take part in planting a flag on the Moon as the Apollo Generation did. She is looking forward to taking part in planting a flag on Mars.

As the world changes, people change along with it. This entire book is a glimpse at how millennials differ from older generations in specific, specialized areas. I see the world slowly becoming more interconnected, more diverse, more tolerant and understanding of differences in the human experience. Millennials may not be fundamentally different from the generations that came before, but I believe the world continues to form and change millennials as millennials form and change the world.

I'd like to believe that each successive generation will become less sexist, less racist, less bigoted against those who are different from themselves, and more accepting of the human race as a whole. By bucking the barriers and constraints that hold us back from progress, we can move forward into the cosmos together. Humanity will still be the same in space as it is on Earth with its same biases, divisiveness, and problems. Hopefully, as humanity continues to mature technologically and as a species, we'll become better versions of ourselves as we leave our nest for the great unknowns beyond.

Generational Divide

While some millennials do not see generational changes, many do. Some millennials suggest these differences are due to age or experience. Many millennials express gratitude that their older colleagues are so willing to share their knowledge and insights will the younger workforce. Some millennials also admire perceived superior work ethics and selfless patriotism in their older colleagues.

Many millennials identify generational differences between their generational peers and their older colleagues. Some millennials report perceived differences in values such as diversity, inclusivity, human rights, environmentalism, and international cooperation. Others millennials see varying motivations in space exploration and a move away from national pride and more toward corporate and personal pride. Some millennials perceive a shift in workforce preferences such as flexible hours and less hierarchical organizational structures.

Some millennials simply feel less patient with their more cynical older colleagues. They view their generation as more optimistic, more open-minded, more willing to try something new, and more eager to challenge the status quo. Millennials want to make rapid progress and change the world, not too different from how previous generations felt about their place in the world.

CHAPTER 11
HOW FAR WE'LL SOAR

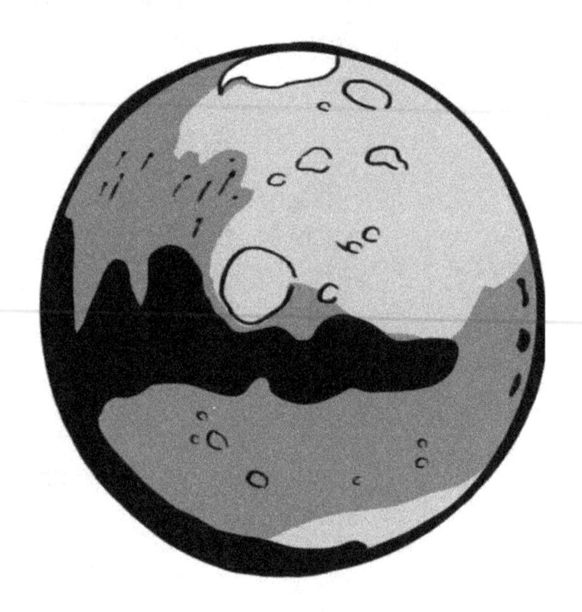

What Will Millennials Achieve?

With so many reflections looking back on the past half a century since humanity first walked on another world, it's time to look forward. There have been monumental successes since the early space age to present day. Each achievement, each failure, and each attempt moves us closer to the dreams of the early space pioneers. Each successive generation carries on, understanding how far the field has come but staring out at the vastness of the cosmos at how far we have yet to go. What will the next half century bring?

Imagine it's 2050. 2060. 2070. 2080. I asked our millennial panel what they believe millennials will achieve in space before they retire, if they retire. I personally can't picture myself retiring from a career I love. How different will the world look a century after NASA first landed astronauts on the surface of the Moon? How far will government and commercial space initiatives go outward in space? What will become routine and commonplace? How much more will space become integrated into the lives of the average person? What will we discover?

Near-Term Predictions

Aerospace engineer Floyd in Iowa believes it is certainly within the realm of possibility that millennials will return humans to the Moon, start a new age of LEO tourism, and study the resources of asteroids. He is more conservative in his predictions than most, believing not much more will happen in the space sector in the next 20 years without weaning ourselves off chemical propulsion rockets. Regardless of how far we go, he believes the work is worth it. We work for a living and we work for a legacy, he declares.

The big pay-off is the world engineer Nicholas in Washington envisions his fellow millennials creating. He hopes to see the next evolution of spacecraft and the creation of extraterrestrial settlements before his days are done. He admits the cost will be high for a generation, but the technological gains will be well worth it. He is inspired by short-term successes as well as long-term accomplishments. Different challenges would arise with different methods and different time scales, but perhaps could be synergistic and bring about serendipitous advances.

Engineer and CEO Jay in Alabama predicts millennials will bring about routine access to space, global connectivity, virtual reality, and space-based computing.

Hopes and Dreams

Corporate communicator Evan in Washington, DC hopes millennials will achieve a unified vision and mission for the space sector. Whether that's establishing humanity as a permanent interplanetary species or committing to exploring interstellar travel, or both, or some other goal, he believes we need a space agenda that doesn't change with the political winds every four to eight years. "Perhaps that means we need a space industry that isn't driven primarily by the government."

Engineer and space policy professional Jane is hopeful and confident that the millennial generation will bring space travel back to the forefront of society as it was during the Apollo era. She envisions personal space travel, research, smallsats, and other advances making space more accessible for the average citizen.

CEO Scott in Florida hopes to see millennials discover a way to travel through space quickly and efficiently, perhaps even with a *Star Trek*-like warp drive. He also believes millennials will improve rocket technology to be as safe and affordable as airline travel is now. He hopes that everyone who can afford an airline ticket today will be able to afford a space ticket before he retires.

Aerospace engineer Yasmin in Florida believes millennials will find a way to make a profit in space from excavating space resources and creating safe space tourism opportunities. She believes these successes will create another boom in the space sector as people become more interested in space and thereby become more willing to invest in space programs.

Engineer Hayley in California believes millennials will build a module or habitat mostly made from space resources. She is inspired by ISRU technologies to 3D print regolith to assist with building infrastructure on the Moon.

Hayley foresees an accident or series of accidents leading to an overhaul of the space insurance and space policy sectors. All new transportation technologies fail at some point and she warns we need to be prepared for the potential backlash. We need to accept the reality that we will lose people in spaceflight. Requiring extraordinary safety measures may hinder humans getting into space so much that we may never leave Earth, she cautions.

Bioengineer Diana in California believes millennials will be able to accomplish the creation of a space habitat capable of supporting a full human life cycle: birth, life, and death. She doesn't expect to see a full human life cycle on a space station before she retires, but she hopes to see the beginnings of one. She would also like to see the establishment of a multinational legal framework for managing space resources including physicochemical resources and land rights. "Getting this done will be a real sign that we're finally extending civilization off planet."

Astronomer Jen in Arkansas hopes new telescopes such as JWST and the *Transiting Exoplanet Survey Satellite* (TESS) will find more Earth-like exoplanets and be able to characterize their atmospheres before she retires.

Geology graduate student Sean in Arizona believes millennials will accomplish Solar System-wide reconnaissance including orbiters around every major planetary body. He also hopes for a renewal of human space exploration to the Moon and Mars.

Astronomy graduate student Jessica in Alabama foresees millennials landing humans on Mars and making further discoveries detecting and understanding gravitational waves. She hopes to see breakthroughs in astrobiology in her lifetime.

Astrobiologist Joshua in California foresees millennials establishing a permanent human presence on Mars. He's hoping to find life on an exoplanet before he retires.

Astronomer Crystal in Maryland believes millennials will send humans to Mars and beyond and find life on another world. Similarly, before engineer Alex in Georgia retires, he hopes to watch the first human landing on Mars and witness the discovery of life elsewhere in our galaxy.

The millennial generation is "itching for our Apollo moment and frustrated it's taking longer than it should," biologist David in California explains. Technologically, he thinks we can pull off a new Moonshot or a "Marsshot", but worries NASA cannot afford it with its limited budget. He has hope that before he retires, humanity will discover indisputable evidence of life on other worlds, forever changing human history. He'd also like to make space exploration more accessible to the masses through virtual reality and other interactive experiences.

Astrophysics student Xzavier in Florida believes millennials will send cargo missions to Mars to prepare for the first Mars astronaut pioneers.

Scientist Anne in Washington believes millennials are capable of successfully using the Moon as a steppingstone to land humans on Mars within her lifetime. "I think we are capable of it. I am less hopeful that the collective will to do it exists."

Student and museum tour guide Walter in Florida envisions science fiction becoming science fact within his lifetime. He hopes new technologies will lead to martian settlements and more frequent spaceflight.

Humans are explorers by nature, engineer Alex in Alabama believes, which is our greatest strength and our greatest flaw. Our drive to explore pushes us to develop amazing technologies, he continues, but we consume everything in our path. To survive, he concludes we need to expand outward and become multi-planetary. He believes we should be more risk-tolerant to make humans a multi-planetary species. By the time the millennial generation is through, he predicts we will develop cislunar infrastructure including transportation and manufacturing, develop a new deep space communication system, and begin settling Mars.

Engineer and data scientist Nikolai in the Czech Republic doesn't ever see himself retiring. He feels fortunate, though. He knows many others of his generation are disadvantaged due to income equality. He sees them endure insults of "lazy" and "entitled" while knowing they will need to work until they die because current social benefits may not be there to support them in their old age. He feels thankful he has a choice to continue working. Although mislabeled as an idealist, he sets high expectations for himself. He strives to work hard, determined to someday see success at his own hands. He sees himself always involved in pursuing advancement of the space industry no matter how old he gets, what his income is, or what his social status is. He's skeptical he will ever see the first humans stepping foot on Mars before he's gone. Yet he's going to keep trying for those impossible goals anyway. For him, enough won't ever be enough.

Businessman Barry in Florida believes millennials are the Mars Generation, working to put footprints on red soil. When the time comes for humans to step foot on Mars, expect to see Barry working right where he is now, working to make it happen.

Planetary scientist Ryan in Missouri envisions millennials will succeed in sending humans to Mars in any capacity: an orbital mission, a one-way mission, or landing astronauts on the surface and bringing them home again. She believes her generation has the drive, passion, and resources to finally accomplish this grand goal.

Engineer Kyle in Washington hopes millennials will send humans to Mars along with the support needed to keep them there. He foresees future space efforts largely being led by industry rather than government.

Scientist Amy in Virginia believes millennials will develop new technologies such as new propulsion methods to accelerate the progress of human space exploration, including the first human mission to Mars. Her money is on SpaceX beating everyone else to the red planet. While she is encouraged by the successes of commercial industry (particularly SpaceX and Blue Origin) innovating with reusable rocketry, she hasn't seen much progress in human spaceflight. This discourages her as she still dreams of someday traveling on a suborbital space tourism flight.

The technology for a human mission to Mars is well within our grasp, aviator Christopher in Florida believes, and he hopes to witness it before he retires. With the advent of increased commercial space transportation, he sees a need for advances in technology and infrastructure to support regular space travel the way we currently support commercial aviation.

Aerospace engineering student Richard in Washington hopes millennials will land humans on Mars in his lifetime. He also expects to see greater commercialization in the space industry which will lead to more accessible spaceflight.

Satellite engineer Adam in Colorado believes the rise of private ventures will drive the costs of spaceflight down. With commercial companies, international cooperation, and increased interest in technology by ever younger members in our society, he foresees humanity achieving the goal of establishing a permanent presence on Mars. He believes his generation will be the one to do it.

Atmospheric scientist Robert in Virginia has high hopes for his generation. He foresees technical breakthroughs allow humans to create a settlement on the Moon and explore the surface of Mars. He envisions commercial spacecraft providing rapid transportation across the globe. He predicts accomplishments he can't yet imagine.

If we play our cards right, aerospace engineer April in Texas believes millennials will establish a permanent human presence on Mars. She also predicts space-related advancements in medicine, material science, agriculture, energy, and other space-benefiting industries. She knows our accomplishments in space will provide a better quality of life on Earth.

Engineer Lyndsay in Virginia believes millennials will see Mars firsthand. She also foresees massive improvements in materials science, spaceflight, small satellites, and our understanding of the Universe.

Software manager Sarah in New Hampshire would like to see her generation begin to settle Mars and develop a fully reusable launch vehicle, keeping in mind safety and environmental values. We humans have a need to understand and explore the world around us, she asserts. To her, space is the next logical step. She believes hard work and dedication will move us forward. She is willing to take risks now early in her career that will pay off in the long run. She has faith in her chosen industry.

Aerospace engineer Christopher in Colorado hopes millennials will establish a sustained human presence on the Moon and Mars before he retires. He also hopes to see space tourism take off through the efforts of emerging space companies. He foresees space-developed technological advancements benefiting Earth such as the ability to grow resilient crops in inhospitable environments.

Space communicator Calvin in New Mexico believes the millennial generation will land humans on Mars and create a permanent space station.

Safety engineer Rachel in Florida believes she will see space tourist floating in habitats in LEO within her lifetime. She expects missions to the Moon and Mars to continue as well.

Businesswoman Crystal in Texas foresees a future with suborbital space tourism, sustained human life on Mars, space stations orbiting Mars, space hotels around Earth, and rapid advances in spaceflight.

Aerospace engineer Darius in Alabama foresees millennials landing humans on Mars and sending astronauts to Europa. He also predicts an extension of the ISS or the creation of next-generation space stations in LEO or potentially at Lagrange points. He also hopes a new space tourism industry will develop and thrive.

Within his lifetime, aerospace engineer Logan in Alabama hopes to witness at least two human missions to near-Mars space, an asteroid mining scouting mission or two, routine LEO access by private companies, frequent space tourism, at least two new space stations, and an increase in robotics on the Moon.

Lofty Hights

Space policy professional Nate in Washington, DC hopes his generation makes space travel somewhat routine for the masses, closer to the routine of air travel, more accessible than it has ever been. "I'm expecting to tell my kids or grandkids what it was like before they could go on a field trip to space." And he hopes millennials take humanity back to the Moon, Mars, and perhaps even to Venus. He will do his part to participate in policy discussions that will help open up the final frontier.

Software engineer Brandon in Washington hopes to see a sustained presence on multiple space stations and on the Moon in the next few decades. Before he retires, he wants to see boot prints on Mars for the first time. He also hopes we send probes to Uranus and Neptune.

Computer engineer Joslyn in Florida believes astronauts will set foot on Mars within her lifetime. She also hopes millennials will launch a new long-range mission to explore the outer edges of our Solar System and beyond.

Engineer Lindsay in Alabama believes millennials will accomplish a Mars sample return mission followed by a human mission to land on Mars. She believes millennials strongly support a human mission to Mars because, "my generation has a strong desire to leave a legacy behind to rival the Apollo missions of the previous generation." She also foresees successful growth in LEO commercial activities such as private space stations and fuel depots. She also hopes to see robotic missions to Europa, Ganymede, and Enceladus, places where life might exist beyond Earth.

Within his lifetime, engineer Vito in Colorado would like to see private space tourism in LEO. He also expects to see an *Apollo 8*-like mission to Mars, sending astronauts to orbit the planet before returning home. He also hopes for advances in planetary science from Mars, Europa, Titan, Uranus, Venus, Enceladus, asteroids, and exoplanets.

Astronomer Rodrigo in New York hopes millennials will send humans to land on Mars and begin to settle it, however primitively. He predicts we will make significant progress toward figuring out if there is life on any of the closest exoplanets. We may even find conclusive evidence of an inhabited planet outside our Solar System, he dreams.

Aerospace engineer Mason in Alabama believes millennials will see the arrival of a commercial space industry reminiscent of the arrival of the commercial aircraft industry in the early- to mid-20th century. He believes millennials will send humans to Mars, asteroids, and back to the Moon.

He foresees robotic vehicles traveling across the Solar System in great numbers. He predicts the space sector in the Middle East and Asia will rise as global space powers equal to the United States, Japan, Europe, and Russia now. These new space powers will drive innovation, technology, and the boundaries of human existence.

Engineer Mark in Virginia has a vision of humans exploring the inner Solar System within his lifetime. He foresees observatories and research stations on the Moon, asteroid mining operations to fuel our pursuit of the frontier, and humans living on Mars.

Geomorphology graduate student Stephanie in California is excited by private space companies growing new industries such as space mining. She hopes millennials will achieve an active space mining industry. She also hopes to see a base on the Moon and a station on Mars.

Biomedical engineer Jordan in British Columbia believes millennials will put humans on Mars. He also foresees vast improvements in harvesting energy from the Sun and minerals from asteroids and other planetary bodies. He also hopes humans will have an established permanent outpost on Mars by the new millennium.

Engineer Nathan in Colorado hopes he will see new methods of space transportation by rail gun, space elevator, or another means of cheaper, easier, better space travel within his lifetime. He expects millennials will send humans to Mars and begin to establish a settlement there. He also hopes to see space mining take off.

Pie in the Sky Hopes

Human factors engineer Victor in Texas believes millennials will begin establishing small settlements on the Moon and Mars, discover more efficient methods of space propulsion, develop better life-support systems, significantly increase human activity in suborbital and orbital space, and boost an international space ethos.

As space becomes more of a global cooperative effort, engineer Altynay in New York believes geopolitics will fade away. She supposes most of her peers share her views and values. She envisions that the millennial generation will advance new space stations and make space tourism become a reality.

Engineer Nicholas in Texas sees a resurgence in the space entrepreneurial spirit. He has high hopes for the millennial generation's potential space accomplishments including frequent space tourism trips, a Mars robotic sample return mission, sustained human habitats on the Moon and Mars, and passenger-carrying spaceships that cruise around the Solar System permanently in varying orbits. He feels blessed to be a part of it.

Millennials seem more open to new and emerging technology, mechanical engineer Chelsea in Florida notes. This openness gives her optimism for the future. She believes millennials will re-energize the space industry and take humans where we have not been before. She foresees making space habitation a reality with surface or orbital bases around the Moon and Mars, and not long after, advancing human exploration to our nearest celestial neighbors.

Before her generation retires and passes the torch to the younger ones, engineer Paige in California hopes humans will have set foot on Mars. She is rooting for NASA, SpaceX, and the international community to establish a continuously crewed based on our neighboring planet. She also envisions robotic missions to Titan, Europa, and elsewhere in the Solar System. She hopes breakthroughs in rocket propulsion will propel us to other stars. "But sadly I think that kind of interstellar exploration is centuries, if not millennia, away."

Communicator Brice in Alabama hopes to see the first human born in space in his lifetime. "I'm hoping to read about it from the Moon."

No Crystal Ball

Ever cautious, businesswoman Carolyn in Colorado declines to speculate about what millennials could accomplish in her lifetime. "Even I know not to look beyond a 10-year time horizon in space!" she quips.

For science reporter Leah in Massachusetts, the nature of her job necessitates touching many areas of space science and the scientific community. That's the part of her job she enjoys the most. Through her work, she finds over and over again that the newest space discoveries and greatest achievements are very difficult if not impossible to predict. Looking back at the last 50 years – sending humans to the Moon, flying robotic spacecraft to visit all of the planets of our Solar System, taking the first close up photos of Mars, the spectacular photos from *Hubble*, growing and eating food in space – who knows what we will achieve in the next 50 years?

The possibilities stretch out before us as they always have. The Moon seems so reachable. The rest of the cosmos is right there, seemingly calling out to us. We predict and project our dreams based on the technology of today and where we think we might go in the coming decades. Perhaps this new technology here and that new advancement there will propel us forward to the stars in new ways and help us probe the mysteries of the worlds beyond ours.

No one knows the future. Many have proven themselves foolish to attempt to predict what is to come. And yet, we still try. We imagine the world as we want it to be or as we believe it could be or much the same as it is now, just a little further along. We hold our priorities high and hope others prioritize those same goals. We look at advancements in other technology areas and wonder if some of those improvements might benefit our industry as well. We try to use logic and reason but we all have our biases that distort our perspectives. We can't see the future clearly no matter how hard we try.

I don't know what the future holds. I don't know what millennials will accomplish in the coming decades. However, I do know that human nature doesn't change. There will still be dreamers and doers. There will still be daredevils and explores. There will still be government bureaucracies and changing political winds. There will still be capitalists and customers. There will still be peacemakers, war fighters, and state secrets. There will still be international collaborations and adversaries fighting colds and hot wars. People will always be people, on Earth, in space, and on any other planetary body we are able to ascend to.

I dream of ordinary citizens soaring above the skies, but that's my own bias. That's where I want to be before I leave this world. That's where I want my descendants, the future generations, to be. That's where I believe humanity belongs, both above our home planet and exploring beyond. May your future be so bright.

Millennials Hopes and Dreams

Some millennials' predictions are conservative. Given the many setbacks over the decades, some question how we'll be able to overcome those barriers to move forward sustainably. After all, the Apollo generation thought we'd be sending humans to Mars by now. By the 1980s, even. What's to say we won't continue to face setbacks and stumbling blocks to prevent our progress forward?

Some millennials dream big. Forget the Moon and Mars. Think deep space. Think interstellar. Think large populations living off-Earth. Science fiction has imagined it. Why shouldn't millennials try to make it happen?

For many millennials, the future is somewhere in between. No one has the ability to peer ahead in time to know just how far we'll go. The world has changed significantly since the 1960s and will continue to change significantly in the coming decades. The only thing that's certain is change and the human drive to keep pressing forward.

About the Author

Laura Seward Forczyk (FOR-zik) has desired to dance on the Moon and explore the stars from a young age. She is the owner of space consulting firm Astralytical specializing in space science, industry, and policy, and offering space career coaching services. Previous consulting topics include space tourism, small satellite launchers, new spaceports, space development priorities and strategies, new technology, and science fiction storytelling.

She is a NASA Subject Matter Expert for planetary science missions. She serves on the advisory boards for the Lifeboat Foundation and the Society of Women in Space

Exploration. She serves as a mentor for the Brooke Owens Fellowship program. She also serves on the organizing committees for three space conferences. She is a frequently-quoted source for news publications and broadcasters.

Prior to forming her own company, she ran the Florida office of international startup working to establish parabolic and suborbital flight at Kennedy Space Center and globally. She has also worked as a scientific analyst for a nonprofit facilitating over 50 experiments on the International Space Station for the benefit of life on Earth.

She has researched astrophysics and planetary science at three NASA centers, flown two parabolic "Zero G" campaigns, conducted geological research in a meteor crater, and earned National Aerospace Training and Research (NASTAR) suborbital astronaut wings in ground training. She is a six-time U.S. Space Camp alumna, a NASA Academy alumna, a former NASA Student Ambassador, and a previous NASA Graduate Student Researchers Program fellow.

She is the founder and former Executive Director of the Georgia Space Alliance. She is also the founder and former President of the Florida Space Development Council.

She earned a bachelor of science in astrophysics from Florida Institute of Technology. She earned a master of science in astrophysics from the University of Alabama in Huntsville researching high-energy emission from gamma-ray bursts. She also founded and serves as President of the UAH chapter of the Society of Physics Students. She conducted doctoral studies in planetary science at the University of Central Florida researching low-energy impacts and regolith (dust) dynamics on the Moon, Mars, and asteroids.

She is a proud wife and mother of two little ones living in Atlanta, Georgia area with three cats and many aquarium creatures. She enjoys crafting, reading, baking, swimming, aerial arts, traveling, participating in her faith, and watching good sci-fi with her family.

Visit astralytical.com to contact Laura and sign up for future book announcements and information.

Connect with Laura:

LinkedIn: linkedin.com/in/lauraforczyk/ and linkedin.com/company/astralytical/

Twitter: @LauraForczyk and @AstralyticalFacebook: facebook.com/Astralytical/

Use the hashtag #SpaceMillennials with a photo of your book or your thoughts on the book and I will retweet or share.